KT-502-532

Health Expectancy and Its Uses

returned on or before
stamped below.

Margaret R. Bone
Office of Population Censuses and Surveys

Andrew C. Bebbington
Personal Social Services Research Unit, University of Kent at Canterbury

Carol Jagger
Department of Epidemiology and Public Health, University of Leicester

Kevin Morgan
Department of Health Care for Elderly People, University of Sheffield

Gerry Nicolaas
Office of Population Censuses and Surveys

London: HMSO

© *Crown copyright 1995*
Applications for reproduction should be made to HMSO's Copyright Unit
First published 1995
ISBN 0 11 702005 2

This study was funded by the Department of
Health. The views expressed in the report are those
of the authors and do not necessarily represent the
views of the Department of Health.

Printed in the United Kingdom for HMSO
Dd301349 8/95 C8 G3397 10170

Contents

Acknowledgements

The authors would like to thank John Charlton (OPCS) for providing mortality data and much helpful advice, Neil Raymond for computing and data analysis for the research reported in chapters 10 and 11, the Latham House general practice for their help with, and the Nuffield Provincial Hospitals Trust for funding the Melton Mowbray Studies.

1 Purpose of the study

1.1 Population aging and its implications for population health

In the last 150 years, this country in common with other industrialised nations has experienced an historically unprecedented decline in mortality. In 1850 expectation of life was about 40 years, today it is over 70. Most of the increase in life expectancy has occurred in the twentieth century: since 1911 about 20 years have been added to expectation of life at birth. A large part of the increase has been due to declines in infant mortality and in deaths from infectious diseases at comparatively young ages. More recently, however, the decline in death rates at older ages has also been accelerating - since the end of World War II in the case of women, and since about 1970 in the case of men. Thus, a woman who survived until age 60 in 1911 could expect a further 15 years of life, compared with 21 years in 1981; for men the expectation of life at age 60 has increased from about 14 to more than 16 years over the same period.

The decline in mortality and changes in the numbers of births have already led to an increase in the number and proportion of older people in the population: in 1911, 1% of the population was aged 75 or over, whereas today, the proportion is 7%. The aging of the population will continue in the first half of the next century when the effect of any further reduction in mortality will be augmented as the 'baby boom' generation, born between 1955 and 1970, reach their sixties; by 2031 the proportion of people aged 75 or more is projected to be 11% (OPCS, 1993).

Pessimists have argued that the aging of the population will be accompanied by a pandemic of degenerative diseases and chronic mental disorders as medical and surgical innovations enable increasing proportions of the unfit to survive (Gruenberg, 1977; Kramer, 1980). Optimists hold that the adoption of healthier lifestyles and scientific advances will result in the compression of morbidity into an increasingly brief period before death (Fries, 1980). In between these two extreme positions are those who argue that the balance between mortality and morbidity will be maintained (Manton, 1982). The scene of the debate is portrayed in Figure 1.1, which also provides the conceptual context for this report (WHO, 1984).

Area A represents for a cohort the number of person years in good health, area B the number with morbidity but no disability, and area C the number of person years with disability. Compression of morbidity occurs if area A increases as a proportion of the total person years of life; expansion, if area A diminishes. Because the topmost curve is shifting upwards and to the right as the expectation of life rises, compression of morbidity can only occur if the two lower curves shift more rapidly in the same direction. It is,

therefore, the relationship between the areas which determines the burden of ill health and dependency on the community and on the quality of individual lives. The way the relationship is evolving has implications for health and social services, the demand for long term care, social security and for the community in general.

Health expectancy is exemplified in Figure 1.1 by e_0** and e_{60}** which refer to the number of expected years, for this cohort, of disability-free life at birth and at age 60, respectively. M_{50}** represents the age to which 50% of this cohort can expect to survive without disability. Health expectancy uniquely combines mortality and morbidity into a single index so that it is independent of the particular age structure of the population to which it is applied. It can, therefore, be used to compare the health states of different populations, to monitor and project the evolution of the healthiness of a particular population, and as an aid to predicting their implications. Health expectancy is the generic term, and specific health expectancy indicators may in principle be constructed for any (usually chronic) health state of interest. Most commonly it has been used to refer to disability-free life expectancy (as illustrated in Figure 1.1) and that is the focus of this report.

1.2 The objectives of this study

The general purpose of the studies brought together in this book was to provide information of use to the Department of Health in any decisions about the adoption of health expectancy as an indicator of the nation's health. The book therefore reviews the main methods of calculating health expectancy, provides examples of a range of applications of the indicator, and draws conclusions about suitable methodologies for the future. Chapters 2 to 5 discuss the policy applications and background to the scientific concern with health expectancy. The next six chapters (6-11) give empirical evidence for the UK and the final four chapters detail the practical requirements and recommendations for adopting health expectancy as an indicator for the UK.

The specific objectives of the work were:

1   to review existing methods of calculating health expectancy (chapter 4);

2   to provide a critical presentation of previously published calculations of health expectancy for this and comparable countries, showing apparent changes over time and differences between populations (chapter 5);

3   to compare trends in health expectancy based on reports of limiting long-standing illness with the inability to perform basic self-care tasks (Activities of Daily Living=ADLs) alone, for older people (aged 65 or more) (chapter 6);

Figure 1.1: The observed mortality and hypothetical morbidity curves for females in the United States of America 1980 (WHO, 1984)

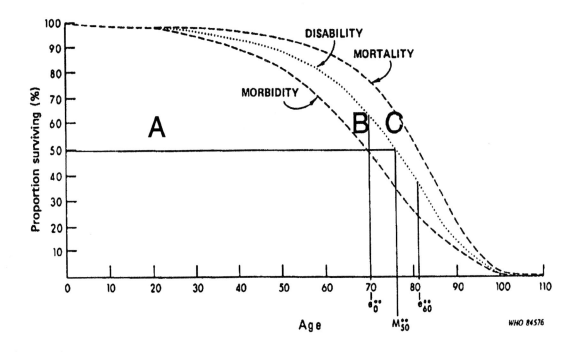

4   to calculate health expectancy from the 1991 Census limiting long-standing illness question for different areas of the country and subgroups of the population (chapter 7);

5   to estimate the effects on health expectancy and life expectancy of deleting major disease categories (chapter 8);

6   to compare health expectancies derived from a variety of definitions of health using both longitudinal and cross-sectional data (chapters 9-11);

7   to discuss methodologies suitable for measuring health expectancy in the future (chapters 12-15).

1.3 Which type of health expectancy?

The appropriate type of health expectancy indicator depends on the specific application concerned. Thus, for monitoring the overall health status of a population a general measure such as disability-free life expectancy may be appropriate; projections of the need for long-term care may require an indicator of independent life expectancy; whereas the effect of a particular health care intervention may best be assessed by examining changes in expectation of life free of the specific condition to which the intervention relates. Chapters 9 to 11 illustrate the use of a range of specific types of health expectancy.

1.4 Recent development of the health expectancy indicator

Although the concept of health expectancy first emerged in the 1960s (Sanders, 1964), the last decade has seen the majority of work in the area, mainly aimed at trying to shed light on whether there has been a compression or expansion of morbidity in the recent past. Much of the work has taken place under the auspices of an international network on health expectancy (Réseau Esperance de Vie en Santé, or REVES). The aims of REVES are to create a common language for health expectancy research, to harmonise methods of calculation and data collection so as to allow comparisons between countries, and to consider how the work on health expectancies might best be presented to aid policy makers concerned with the provision of services and the formulation of preventive strategies (Mathers and Robine, 1993). The terms and abbreviations used in this report are in line with the standardised terminology proposed by REVES.

2 Policy applications of measures of health expectancy

The measurement of health expectancy is a basic tool of analysis which provides a means of measuring the state of public health in general or of particular population groups which is independent of the age structure, in a way that has a direct interpretation for the lives of individuals. The purpose of this chapter is to identify policy issues to which measures of health expectancy could be usefully applied. These policy applications include:

- Monitoring health trends and the compression of morbidity;
- Issues of equity between populations, particularly between regions, social classes, and ethnic groups;
- Health care planning - predicting the health status of the population in the short term and projecting them over the longer term;
- Health care outcomes, indicating the improvements in healthy life that might be achievable through alternative health programmes.

These issues are very salient to monitoring the policy objectives of the UK "Health of the Nation" programme.

Health, in the present context, is an inclusive term. It covers chronic ill-health, handicap, disability, death; it may be confined to specific diseases or disease groups, or it may refer to health-related events such as entry into long-term institutional care. All of these may form the basis of defining health states: obviously the choice will be determined by the application.

Later chapters will describe how health expectancy can be measured from both prevalence data on health states and evidence about the incidence of change in health. It will be explained why incidence based measures are superior. Prevalence data however, are widely available from cross-sectional studies and we shall be illustrating the application of health expectancy based on prevalence data to some of these policy issues. In contrast there is as yet no source of information at a national level about the incidence of health changes, other than for mortality and a few specific diseases. What is required for this is a registration system or a longitudinal survey. There are other closely related measures that can only be measured with incidence data. Examples of health expectancy based on longitudinal studies of the elderly at a local level are provided in chapter 11.

A distinction is drawn in what follows between what is already achievable using measures based on available prevalence rates, and what would be possible using health expectancy and related measures derived from incidence rates. The latter is particularly pertinent to the case for a national longitudinal database presented in chapter 12 of this book.

2.1 Health trends

Comparisons through time provide a means of measuring the state of public health in general or of particular population groups, and so may be used to monitor the broad impact of health and social policy. Combined with information about mortality, health expectancy measures serve to test whether improvements in health care and social and economic conditions are postponing the onset of disabilities into an increasingly brief period before death, or are simply preserving the lives of the unfit: in terms of Figure 1.1 (page 2) whether a compression or expansion of morbidity is occurring. Population subgroups monitored may include those of people in particular health states, so that the general effect of policies directed towards the rehabilitation of people with specific conditions or disabilities can be assessed.

This has so far been one of the most common applications of health expectancy. In chapter 5 the evidence from a number of countries is reviewed, and in chapter 6 detailed results from time series for this country are presented and discussed in the context of the compression of morbidity debate.

Health prognosis

There are two other concepts closely associated with health expectancy, which like it translate the experience of populations into the experience of individuals. These are

- Prognosis, the expected duration in a health state *given the initial health state*. (For example, what is the expectation of healthy life of someone aged 65 who is currently healthy).

- Lifetime risk, of ever experiencing a particular health state or event before death.

Neither of these can be calculated from prevalence data. However their estimation from incidence data is practicable: for example Zdeb (1977) used this method to show that the lifetime risk of developing cancer increased from 18 to 27 per cent for male residents of New York between 1950 and 1970.

Among other uses, prognosis from a given health state is useful in drawing attention to the extent of improvement in health status and recovery of independence at older ages. Prognosis is usually calculated from cohort data; by a long-term follow up study of people diagnosed with specific health conditions. Most major physical and mental diseases have been investigated in this way. It is, however, also possible to use short run incidence data, e.g. of death rates for people with a particular health condition. This approach is suitable for conditions where the increased risk of death is not related to the length of time for which the subject has had the condition (Haberman, 1983). The method can be used to make predictions for the long-term consequences of other types of health related life-event such as impairment; or, as in the example above, the expectations for someone who is fully healthy.

Life-time risk is also of interest, particularly for health conditions that are inherently unusual, such as the risk of entering institutional care. Such predictions are of considerable value for personal planning and actuarial calculations. There is concern that reduction in some diseases, such as chronic heart disease, may result in an increase in the life-time risk of other conditions such as senile dementia. Incidence data can be used to model the likely consequences of reduction of particular diseases, not only in terms of their effect on overall life expectancy and healthy life expectancy, but in terms of the resulting change in the life-time costs of health care, which may well be increased if quick-acting diseases of late middle age are replaced by slower acting conditions of old age.

2.2 Equity and resource allocation

Comparisons between population groups allow variations between countries, regions, social classes, and so forth to be identified. For this reason measures of health expectancy have an important potential role in resource allocation decisions. Comparisons between social classes provide a useful addition to understanding of social justice and the need to target social welfare. What has in part held things back has been the lack of a health indicator that is simple, can be measured routinely on population subgroups, and is robust to assumptions of detail. Later chapters shows that we are now close to having such measures.

Comparisons between population groups can also be of value in the search for common risk factors and other variables which influence risks. Because health expectancy summarises information about mortality and morbidity in a way which is independent of the age structure of the population to which it relates, it is a particularly appropriate basis for making such comparisons. It has been used extensively in international comparisons, and is now increasingly being used for comparing areas and population subgroups within countries (e.g. Crimmins et al, 1994; van Oyen et al, 1994; Boshuizen et al, 1994; Valkonen et al, 1994). In chapter 5, health expectancies for this country are compared with those found in others. Variations in health expectancy between different regions and local authority areas of England and Wales are shown in chapter 7, and inequalities explained by differences in the socio-economic composition of their populations.

Resource allocation: health

One potential application is to resource allocation in the National Health Service. The English system of allocating health resources for the NHS is undergoing a major change. The new method (Carr-Hill et al, 1994) in essence estimates the level of health need of areas based on a range of indicators of need, according to their empirical relationship to actual utilization at a local level (but adjusting for certain supply effects). Allowance is made for likely unit costs of health interventions.

This approach targets resources towards those areas where there is the greatest expectation of ill health (or more accurately, where the cost implications of ill health are the greatest). This is not necessarily the same thing as targeting resources where the expectation of healthy life is lowest. It is certainly arguable that an equitable resource allocation system should be concerned with this second criterion of equity as well as with the first. Figure 7.1 in chapter 7 (page 37) shows that the areas of highest ill health are for the most part those of lowest health expectancy. However, there are plenty of exceptions. Areas in the lower left corner of the figure have unexceptional amounts of ill-health but the lowest expectations of healthy life. For example, certain areas of London have an age-standardised limiting long-standing illness rate well below the national average, yet there is a comparatively low healthy life expectancy.

Estimating the inherent healthfulness, and hence the health needs of areas on the basis of health expectancy, will require further analysis for two reasons. The first is that on its own, the approach provides no means of establishing what is an appropriate level of additional funding to an unhealthy area in order to achieve a given level of improvement. The second concerns the effect of internal migration, particularly of healthy people around the time of retirement. As noted in chapter 4, prevalence based estimates of health expectancy are affected by the past history of individuals. This will undoubtedly exaggerate the apparent healthfulness of areas such as the south west of England which will attract such people. Whether this is a large effect is unknown. A measure of health expectancy based on age specific incidence (rather than prevalence) rates would avoid this problem.

Resource allocation: standard spending assessments

Another example is Standard Spending Assessments (SSAs) for personal social services. These have been based on estimates of the resources required for tackling current levels of need. The resource allocation approach is to estimate the expenditure required by local authorities to enable them to provide a standard level of services to their resident populations. These estimates, as with the revised NHS formula, are mostly based on need indicators derived from the Census and related sources.

A general problem with this approach in that the current pattern of need is inevitably affected by services that have already been provided. This complicates any attempt to establish the underlying level of need in the community in a way which is difficult to unravel. This is true particularly of the types of health problem that are apt to be long-term. (Although Carr-Hill et al (1994) allow the simultaneity of demand and supply, the possibility of past supply affecting current need is not considered in their formulation - presumably because most health conditions are not long-term. But of course a successful health intervention will often have long-term implications).

A longitudinal survey or recording system which reveals transitions in levels of need offers a means of surmounting the problem. A particular example of current concern is that of elderly and disabled people with high levels of needs for which residential care might be considered appropriate. Cross-sectional surveys of needs invariably face the problem that it is impossible to tell of people already in residential care whether they would have been judged to need a high cost service under a nationally standard level of service, since many of the circumstances which were relevant to that judgement, such as the level of informal support available to them living at home, no longer apply. Studies of admission have been considered as a means of identifying the criteria associated with admission, and indeed this approach worked well in determining a similar needs indicator for children in care (Bebbington and Miles, 1988). However, a cross-sectional study of the elderly at the point of admission is not satisfactory, since it is so often impractical to establish for this age group their underlying or long-term circumstances during a time of crisis. What is required instead is an understanding of the circumstances that will put people at risk of admission within the foreseeable future, and it is here that a prospective longitudinal data would be specially useful. Then an equitable judgement about the appropriate level of provision in future is based on predictions of the numbers currently at risk.

2.3 Social care planning

Health expectancy predicts the duration of life at levels of illness or disability at which care interventions may be necessary, and the future need for services. Assumptions about trends in health expectancy at older ages are particularly significant when the elderly population is increasing rapidly.

Long-term resource needs

The outstanding example of this application of health expectancy is for describing the expected liability of elderly people for long-term care as a basis for designing long-term care insurance. For the purpose of estimating future resource needs, definitions of ill-health are appropriately chosen to correspond to the thresholds for care needs or eligibility for benefits. (Liu et al, 1990). Nuttall et al (1993) have developed estimates of the future costs of long-term care in the UK, which show the sensitivity of these estimates to different assumptions and the potential seriousness of the situation in 20 or 30 years time under different assumptions. The sensitivity of their findings seems most acute in relation to different assumptions about trends in rates into and out of ill-health, but at present this is the area where hard information is in shortest supply. This is an example where incidence data is badly needed. A longitudinal survey would, as we have already observed, provide estimates of the current age-specific incidence rates which would start to remedy this important gap. However, the major concern at present concerns the *trends* in these incidence rates: in effect whether there is compression or expansion of morbidity. Longitudinal cohort data are necessary for projecting trends. Methods of projection and forecasting which involve health expectancy have been developed with the US Long-Term Care Survey

(Manton and Stallard, 1988), but do not yet appear to have been applied to resource need prediction. But at present there are no relevant longitudinal data at the national level in this country which could provide the basis for making projections.

Projections of the health state of the population over the longer term aid planning of resources to meet health needs. Methods of projection and forecasting which involve health expectancy have been developed (Manton and Stallard, 1988), and attempts to apply methods of projection are now being made (Deeg et al, 1994; Heathcote and McDermid, 1994; Wilkins et al, 1994; van den Berg Jeths, 1994).

Service planning

A similar approach can be used for predicting the future market for particular services, such as residential care. In this case, however, it is not eligibility criteria that will determine demand, but rather the future incidence of people with that *combination* of circumstances which makes them likely to want particular forms of care. Health expectancy predicts the duration of life in such circumstances: longitudinal data could also provide the information about what are the circumstances which are associated with subsequent uptake of particular services.

2.4 Health outcomes

Health expectancy may be used to predict the improvement in years of health potentially achievable by alternative health care strategies, targeted either in terms of particular health conditions causing disability, or of particular population subgroups; and hence indicate the cost-effectiveness of such alternative strategies. In relation to Figure 1.1, the question would be, which strategy was likely to bring about the greatest reduction in the areas of morbidity or disability as proportions of the total area of person years.

Hitherto, this application has been addressed to very broad issues: first, the relative effects of changing mortality rates, the incidence of disability, and rates of improvement in functioning on the health state of the population (Crimmins et al, 1992a); and second, the effects of eliminating major categories of disease (Mathers, 1991). The results of applying the second procedure to the British population are given in chapter 8. Chapter 3 describes some of the main areas where information will most urgently be needed. A more elaborate approach which additionally shows the consequences for the health of the population of removing specific risks and of adding specific interventions has also been proposed (Wolfson and Manton, 1992).

2.5 Conclusion

In this section we have described a number of policy applications for which health expectancy measures are potentially useful. We have also described how it can be used to assist individuals in making more informed decisions about their own health behaviour and health futures. Some of these applications can be tackled with existing prevalence data, but our ability to answer others requires knowledge about incidence rates on the health of our society, or at least would be improved by such knowledge. Data are needed not only on general measures of disability and ill-health but also on the common causes of chronic morbidity in our society: CVD, vision and hearing defects, depression, dementia, osteoarthritis. These data must be available for population subgroups: localities, ages, social class, etc given concerns with equity in health and social care. Longitudinal data for these conditions would enable us to answer questions about whether we are *currently* doing better or worse than in the past (rather than several or many years after changes have occurred) in a useful manner for the monitoring and development of health and social policy.

3 Developments in the prevention and treatment of chronic disease

In recent years both the incidence and the survival associated with many of the more common disabling conditions of later life have been influenced by a variety of social and medical factors. Changes in lifestyle, developments in geriatric medicine and the organisation of services, improvements in drug therapy and surgical intervention, and changes in clinical attitudes towards the older patient have all played a part. In this section we examine some of the evidence linking such changes with health outcome. The aim, however, is not to provide a detailed review of developments in prevention and treatment. Rather, by focusing on selected examples of changing dynamics in physical and psychiatric morbidity, our aim is to highlight evidence that rates of transition into (and out of) states of disabling illness are unlikely to be characterised by stability in the coming decades.

3.1 Causes of disability in later life

A recent review of the health of elderly people in the United Kingdom (MRC, 1994) identified the consequences of cardiovascular and cerebrovascular disease, sensory problems (particularly vision and hearing), osteoarthritis, osteoporosis, incontinence, dementia and depression as the major causes of disability in later life. While research attention to each of these conditions continues to grow, the empirical data are considerably better developed in some areas than in others. As regards cerebrovascular and cardiovascular events, for example, evidence of continuing change in the natural history of stroke and heart disease is available from epidemiological studies, secondary analyses, clinical trials, and service evaluations. In addition to the disabilities imposed by physical illness, the functional limitations which result from psychiatric conditions also provide an important area of concern and research. In the present brief overview, then, particular emphasis will be placed on stroke, heart disease, and dementia as exemplars of conditions causing disability.

Stroke

Acute stroke represents one of the most common causes of mortality and morbidity among older people in the UK, contributing substantially to subjective reports of chronic ill health (Goddard and Savage, 1994). Sandercock and Linley (1993) estimate that of 100,000 first strokes in the UK each year, 60% of patients die, or show dependence in activities of daily living after 6 months. Nevertheless, epidemiological trends clearly show a continuing decline in stroke mortality since the early 1960s (Casper et al, 1992; Niessen et al, 1993). Although the reasons underlying falling stroke mortality throughout this period are not clearly understood, lifestyle changes and improvements in "socio-economic resources" may well account for the earlier trends (Casper et al, 1992), while the benefits of antihypertensive therapy are thought to contribute, albeit in a minor way, to the more

recent gains. That the benefits of antihypertensive drug management will continue to affect both morbidity and mortality from stroke is strongly suggested by the available clinical trials evidence (Farnsworth and Hesletine, 1993). Continued reductions in stroke mortality and morbidity can also be expected from the modification of other risk factors. Using state event models to examine Dutch national data sets, Niessen et al (1993), for example, predict that patterns of stroke incidence will continue to decline in the Netherlands up to 2005, and conclude that there are "..still benefits to be gained from large-scale hypertension control and reduction of smoking". At the population level, changing stroke mortality has been shown to have a significant impact upon measures of disability-free life expectancy (DFLE). Barendregt et al (1994), modelling cross-sectional data, have shown that increased survival following stroke and heart disease substantially reduces DFLE in older age groups. (However, as the same analyses showed, paradoxically, no impact on DFLE at birth, the authors argue strongly for the use of superior multistate methods based on longitudinal data.)

Improvements in survival through the clinical management of acute stroke can also be expected in the coming decades, though at present the style of care appears to be associated with more clear-cut advantages than specific drug therapies. Langhorne et al (1993), for example, in a meta analysis of trials comparing stroke units with conventional care conclude that dedicated rehabilitation in specialised units is associated with a "... sustained reduction in mortality". Prominent among the drug treatments proposed for acute (ischaemic) stroke is antithrombotic therapy, which has been shown to reduce often fatal post-stroke events. From an overview of 15 controlled trials however, Sandercock et al (1993) acknowledge that such treatments can reduce mortality and disability (through reductions in infarct size, deep vein thrombosis and pulmonary embolism), but point out that risks of disabling and fatal haemorrhagic transformation (of the original infarct) may negate these benefits. Further research in this area is aimed at both refining and targeting these advantages, and it is not an unreasonable assumption that such developments will further increase survival and decrease dependence after stroke.

Heart disease

Continuing reduction in morbidity and mortality from the modification of risk factors in those at high risk of coronary heart disease (particularly hypertension, smoking, high serum cholesterol levels, and being overweight) are also likely to continue into future decades. State-transition simulations recently reported by Tsvat et al (1991), predict gains in life expectation (at age 35) of 2.3 years for at-risk men who stop smoking, 1.1-5.3 years for those who reduce their diastolic blood pressure to 88 mm Hg, 0.5-4.2 years for those who reduce serum cholesterol levels to 200 mg/dl, and 0.7-1.7 years for those who achieve ideal body weight. Corresponding gains for at-risk women were 2.8, 0.9-5.7, 0.4-6.3, and 0.5-1.1 years respectively.

That such risk factors continue to influence the likelihood of coronary heart disease (CHD) in old age has been emphasised in several recent analyses. Comparing younger (35-49) and older (65+) patients in a case-control study, Applegate et al (1991) found that smoking, hypertension, total cholesterol, and left ventricular hypertrophy were all significant risk factors in both groups. Evidence from the Whitehall study of male civil servants (Shipley et al, 1991) also suggests that cholesterol reduction in late middle age may reduce risk of CHD in old age. The benefits to (at risk) older individuals of risk factor modifications have also been demonstrated for blood pressure reduction (Farnsworth, 1993) and smoking cessation (Hermanson et al, 1988). Collectively, then, such data indicate that programmes of risk factor treatment may have a significant impact on future CHD mortality and morbidity rates not only if initiated in middle age, but also if initiated in later life, though the evidence continues to suggest caution (Beaglehole, 1991).

Though risk factor modification may help to improve mortality and morbidity from CHD, socio-economic and demographic factors are likely to act against this. Declines in death rates are not yet appearing in manual workers, though decreasing rates are appearing in the higher socio-economic groups. Asian immigrants have significantly higher risk of mortality and morbidity from CHD and the aging of this subgroup of the population will put more at risk of CHD.

Although elderly people have often been denied access to specialist investigation and treatment for CHD on the assumption that benefits would be low, several recent studies indicate that such assumptions are ill founded (Boon, 1991). The benefits of thrombolytic agents post myocardial infarction, for example, have been shown to be age independent (ISIS-2, 1988). As attitudes towards age-barriers in treatment change, it is, again reasonable to expect changes in survival following acute myocardial infarction in older patients. Indeed, such attitudinal 'shifts' in the management of late life heart disease may exemplify a more general change in decisions to treat elderly patients. Grimley Evans (1991) has recently argued that physiology, not chronological age, should determine levels and styles of care, reflecting a growing body of evidence that treatment strategies formerly reserved for younger patients can be successfully deployed in elderly populations. Clearly, then, changing trends in the availability of effective treatment for older people cannot but affect levels of morbidity and mortality in old age.

Dementia

Although neglected for some time, clinical and research attention to dementia has developed rapidly over the past 10 years, with epidemiological data clearly identifying the condition as a major public health issue. From cross-sectional data Roelands et al (1994) have recently estimated that while 65 year old Belgians have a life expectancy of 16.4 years,

they have a dementia-free life expectancy of 15.3 years. By the age of 85+, however, it was found that 20% of remaining life for men, and 30% for women, would be spent in the demented state. Though still incurable, it is possible that two factors may influence future survival rates associated with this condition, delaying the transition from illness to death. First, the developments of new therapeutics which slow, but do not reverse the deterioration. And second, refinements in broader clinical management and supportive care which optimise post onset life expectation.

Evidence for the latter has been provided by Christie and Wood (1990) who report a trend in increased survival among hospitalised patients with dementia from the 1940s, through the 1970s, and 1980s. However, a review of international data (van Dijk et al, 1991) found no evidence of increased survival for dementia as a whole, but acknowledged that there may be an improved survival for patients with Alzheimer's disease specifically. Drug therapies which appear, even minimally, to modify the dementing process (as expressed, usually, in changes in cognitive and ADL performance scores), may also have an impact on survival, though data addressing this issue are limited (van Dijk et al, 1991). Nevertheless the value of developing, and marketing, therapeutics which may effectively extend a period of disability, without fundamentally modifying the disabling disease, has been questioned (Spagnoli, 1991) and may ultimately be of considerable policy importance.

3.2 Conclusion

On the basis of the examples provided it is reasonable to conclude that current cross-sectionally assessed transitions into states of disability, and from states of disability to death, providing as they do snapshots from a changing clinical and cultural milieu, are unlikely to remain constant over the next 20 years or so. The additional effects of cohort differences in disease vulnerability (for example in osteoporosis), and the development of government health policy (reductions in CHD and stroke mortality among those aged 65-74 of at least 30% and 40% respectively between 1990-2000 are specifically targeted in "Health of the Nation"), should also be considered. In addition, it is worth pointing to likely temporal variations in another, neglected, transition. Though conceptually similar, health expectancy and life expectancy differ in at least one important respect. As Rogers et al (1990) point out, while resurrection has never been a problem in constructing life tables, recovery presents a real challenge when modelling health expectancy. As treatment options for elderly people become both more widely available, and more refined, transitions from illness states to health states may also contribute substantially to the changing natural history of disability in later life.

4 Existing methods of calculating health expectancy

Two main ways are used to calculate health expectancy: one is the Sullivan method (Sullivan, 1971), and the other is the multistate life table method (Manton and Stallard, 1988; Schoen, 1988). Sullivan's method is the most commonly used because it is applied to cross-sectional data on the prevalence of disability which are widely available from regular surveys and censuses, for example, the General Household Survey (GHS), the English Health Survey and the 1991 Census. In certain circumstances (that is, if the rates at which people become ill, recover and die remain relatively stable over the long term) it produces good health expectancy measures for monitoring the health of a population over time, and for comparing the health of different populations. All the results presented in chapters 5 to 8 and chapter 10 are based on the Sullivan method.

The use of prevalence data assumes that people of a given age will later experience the same prevalence of morbidity as those older than themselves. This is unsatisfactory because current prevalence depends on the past history of cohorts; for example, the decline in smoking means that younger cohorts will not experience the same prevalence of smoking related diseases and any consequent disabilities as those now in their 60s and 70s. A truer picture of the way the health status of the population is evolving is given by the rates at which people are currently becoming ill or recovering, and more generally by the rates of transitions between health states. It is these rates which drive the future evolution of prevalence rates, and which are affected by interventions long before the impact on prevalence is manifested. Transition rates are therefore essential for making projections and will produce much better and more informative estimates than prevalence rates of the effect of health care and other interventions. In general, it is only if transition rates are stable over a very long period that cross-sectional prevalence data will yield measures of health expectancy which are adequate for many of the policy applications identified in chapter 2.

Health expectancy is calculated from transition rates by the multistate life table method. It is applied to longitudinal data, which are rare at the national level in this - and most other - countries. It yields much more information than the Sullivan method about the dynamics of the disability process and the components of change. It is therefore superior to the Sullivan method for assessing the effects on populations of different health intervention strategies, and it is the only method of making realistic predictions of the future needs for health and social services for chronic morbidity and disability.

The multistate method can be used to calculate the health expectancy of a population at a particular time (like the Sullivan method), or to calculate the health expectancy of successive cohorts of the population as they pass through life

- or its later years. The second application improves understanding of health trends and longer term projections of the health state of the population.

Both methods of calculating health expectancy are based on that for life expectancy, which is one of the values produced in a standard life table. Just as the latter summarises information about mortality, so these methods summarise information about both mortality and morbidity.

In what follows we describe each method in more detail, and compare their advantages and disadvantages.

4.1 The life table and life expectancy

To appreciate the difference between the Sullivan and multistate life table methods, it is useful to recall features of the standard current life table.

The current life table, among other things, shows for someone of a given age (e.g. at birth) the further years of life they can on average expect - *if they were to experience the currently prevailing age-specific mortality rates*. The basic information required to construct a life table is a series of age-specific mortality rates, derived from:

- the numbers in the population at successive ages at a given time point (e.g. the midpoint of a specific year - often a census year);

- the numbers of deaths occurring at each age during a defined surrounding period (e.g. the whole calendar year).

Life tables are usually constructed for males and females separately, and single years of age or wider intervals (usually five years) may be used. An example of a life table showing three key values is given in Figure 4.1 (OPCS, 1987). Life expectancy is shown in the e_x column at the end of each block of figures; so, for example, life expectancy at birth for males in 1980-82 was just over 71 years. The key values are shown in Box 4.1.

The mortality rate $(_nq_x)$ is the basic function of the life table, from which all other functions are derived.

During a period of declining mortality, life expectancy derived from *current* life tables will underestimate people's actual life expectancy. This can eventually be calculated from *cohort* life tables by using the actual age-specific death rates experienced by particular birth cohorts. The difference between current and cohort life table values for life expectancy at birth is illustrated in Figure 4.2. As an example, from contemporary current life tables, life expectancy

Figure 4.1: English Life Tables No.14: 1980-82

Age	Males l_x	q_x	e_x	Females l_x	q_x	e_x
0	100,000	.01271	71.043	100,000	.00984	77.002
1	98,729	.00085	70.956	99,016	.00072	76.766
2	98,645	.00051	70.016	98,945	.00045	75.820
3	98,594	.00038	69.051	98,900	.00031	74.855
4	98,557	.00035	68.077	98,869	.00025	73.878
5	98,522	.00032	67.101	98,844	.00022	72.896
6	98,490	.00030	66.123	98,822	.00020	71.913
7	98,461	.00027	65.142	98,802	.00019	70.927
8	98,434	.00025	64.160	98,783	.00019	69.941
9	98,409	.00024	63.176	98,764	.00018	68.954
10	98,385	.00024	62.191	98,746	.00018	67.966
11	98,362	.00024	61.206	98,728	.00018	66.979
12	98,338	.00026	60.221	98,710	.00018	65.991
13	98,312	.00029	59.237	98,693	.00019	65.002
14	98,283	.00034	58.254	98,675	.00022	64.014
15	98,250	.00041	57.274	98,653	.00026	63.028
16	98,210	.00053	56.297	98,628	.00030	62.044
17	98,158	.00102	55.326	98,598	.00033	61.062
18	98,057	.00111	54.382	98,566	.00035	60.082
19	97,948	.00102	53.442	98,531	.00035	59.103
20	97,849	.00093	52.496	98,497	.00035	58.124
21	97,757	.00087	51.545	98,462	.00036	57.144
22	97,672	.00083	50.589	98,427	.00036	56.164
23	97,591	.00081	49.631	98,392	.00037	55.184
24	97,511	.00081	48.671	98,356	.00038	54.204
25	97,432	.00081	47.710	98,318	.00039	53.225
26	97,353	.00082	46.749	98,280	.00041	52.245
27	97,273	.00083	45.787	98,239	.00043	51.267
28	97,192	.00084	44.824	98,197	.00045	50.288
29	97,110	.00086	43.862	98,153	.00048	49.311
30	97,027	.00088	42.899	98,105	.00052	48.335
31	96,941	.00091	41.936	98,054	.00056	47.359
32	96,853	.00094	40.974	98,000	.00060	46.385
33	96,762	.00099	40.012	97,941	.00065	45.413
34	96,666	.00105	39.051	97,877	.00071	44.442
35	96,564	.00113	38.092	97,807	.00078	43.474
36	96,455	.00123	37.134	97,732	.00085	42.507
37	96,337	.00134	36.179	97,649	.00093	41.543
38	96,208	.00148	35.227	97,557	.00103	40.581
39	96,065	.00165	34.279	97,457	.00114	39.622
40	95,907	.00184	33.335	97,346	.00127	38.667
41	95,731	.00206	32.395	97,223	.00141	37.715
42	95,534	.00231	31.461	97,086	.00157	36.768
43	95,313	.00260	30.532	96,933	.00176	35.825
44	95,066	.00293	29.611	96,763	.00196	34.887
45	94,787	.00332	28.696	96,573	.00219	33.955
46	94,472	.00376	27.790	96,361	.00245	33.028
47	94,117	.00425	26.893	96,125	.00274	32.108
48	93,717	.00481	26.006	95,862	.00305	31.195
49	93,266	.00545	25.129	95,569	.00340	30.289
50	92,758	.00615	24.264	95,244	.00378	29.390
51	92,187	.00694	23.411	94,884	.00419	28.500
52	91,548	.00781	22.571	94,486	.00465	27.618
53	90,833	.00877	21.744	94,047	.00514	26.744
54	90,037	.00982	20.932	93,564	.00567	25.880
55	89,152	.01098	20.135	93,034	.00624	25.025
56	88,173	.01224	19.353	92,453	.00686	24.178
57	87,094	.01361	18.586	91,819	.00752	23.342
58	85,909	.01509	17.836	91,129	.00824	22.515
59	84,612	.01670	17.101	90,379	.00901	21.698
60	83,199	.01843	16.383	89,564	.00986	20.890
61	81,666	.02028	15.681	88,681	.01077	20.093
62	80,010	.02229	14.995	87,726	.01176	19.307
63	78,226	.02448	14.326	86,695	.01284	18.530
64	76,312	.02687	13.672	85,582	.01400	17.765
65	74,261	.02949	13.036	84,384	.01528	17.010
66	72,071	.03238	12.417	83,095	.01669	16.266
67	69,738	.03555	11.815	81,708	.01828	15.533
68	67,259	.03903	11.232	80,214	.02008	14.813
69	64,634	.04285	10.668	78,603	.02212	14.106
70	61,864	.04703	10.123	76,864	.02443	13.414
71	58,955	.05160	9.597	74,987	.02704	12.737
72	55,913	.05658	9.092	72,959	.02998	12.077
73	52,749	.06198	8.607	70,772	.03329	11.435
74	49,480	.06783	8.143	68,416	.03698	10.811
75	46,123	.07416	7.699	65,886	.04110	10.207
76	42,703	.08096	7.275	63,178	.04566	9.622
77	39,246	.08827	6.872	60,294	.05072	9.059
78	35,781	.09610	6.489	57,236	.05637	8.516
79	32,343	.10445	6.126	54,010	.06271	7.994
80	28,965	.11334	5.782	50,623	.06982	7.495
81	25,682	.12278	5.458	47,089	.07779	7.020
82	22,528	.13278	5.152	43,426	.08669	6.570
83	19,537	.14333	4.865	39,661	.09661	6.146
84	16,737	.15440	4.596	35,829	.10750	5.749
85	14,153	.16591	4.345	31,978	.11922	5.381
86	11,805	.17776	4.112	28,165	.13160	5.042
87	9,706	.18986	3.895	24,459	.14448	4.731
88	7,863	.20215	3.693	20,925	.15772	4.446
89	6,274	.21453	3.506	17,625	.17116	4.186
90	4,928	.22693	3.331	14,608	.18468	3.949
91	3,810	.23929	3.167	11,910	.19814	3.733
92	2,898	.25153	3.012	9,550	.21143	3.534
93	2,169	.26374	2.863	7,531	.22442	3.352
94	1,597	.27632	2.718	5,841	.23703	3.18
95	1,156	.28971	2.574	4,457	.24914	3.020
96	821	.30430	2.431	3,346	.26096	2.864
97	571	.32044	2.288	2,473	.27331	2.706
98	388	.33844	2.145	1,797	.28715	2.545
99	257	.35853	2.004	1,281	.30330	2.380
100	165	.38087	1.865	893	.32252	2.210
101	102	.40551	1.729	605	.34538	2.038
102	61	.43241	1.597	396	.37231	1.866
103	34	.46140	1.471	248	.40349	1.698
104	19	.49214	1.350	148	.43881	1.535
105	9	.52414	1.236	83	.47780	1.380
106	4	.55667	1.129	43	.51960	1.234
107	2	.58874	1.029	21	.56277	1.100
108	1	.61896	.935	9	.60521	.976
109			4		.64382	.862
110			1		.67391	.755

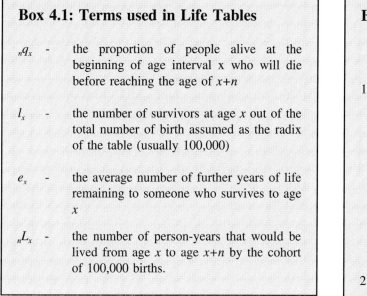

for male children born in 1911 in England and Wales was 52 years: in fact, subsequent cohort life tables show that their actual life expectancy has been 56 years. For females born in the same year, the difference is greater: the current life table value was 55 years, whereas their actual life expectancy has been 62 years (OPCS, 1994). Cohort life tables, although of historical interest, are calculated because they are used for making population projections and for projecting the future cost of pensions.

In principle, as will be described, the two approaches to calculating life expectancy - from current or cohort life tables - can be applied to calculations of health expectancy.

4.2 Health expectancy

The Sullivan Method

Unlike conventional life tables, Sullivan's method uses prevalence rates; that is, in the case of morbidity. As noted earlier, the proportion with morbidity at each age at any one time depends on the past history of the population - for example, experience of an earlier war or epidemic. Consequently, health expectancy calculated in this way may be biased. It represents the current health status of the population, but takes no account of current rates of becoming ill and of remission, unless they have remained unchanged for a long period. If rates have remained unchanged, and measurement is accurate in both cases, Sullivan's method produces the same health expectancy values as the more elaborate multistate method; otherwise the Sullivan indicator lags behind the multistate version (Mathers, 1991; Barendregt, 1994). Simulations suggest, however, that health expectancies derived by Sullivan's method will be very similar to those calculated by the multistate method even when morbidity and remission rates (transition rates) have changed, *providing* the changes have been smooth and relatively regular over the longer term (Robine and Mathers, 1993). It is for this reason that it was said earlier that in *certain* circumstances (i.e. where there are no abrupt changes in transition rates) Sullivan's method produces good health

expectancy measures for monitoring the health of a population over time and for comparing the health of different populations.

The information needed to apply the Sullivan method is:

•   data from current life tables

•   the age specific prevalence of disability in the population, which is often available from a regular survey or census (although estimates may need to be made for the population in institutions).

Essentially, the method involves partitioning life expectancy into years with and without morbidity. The method of calculation is shown in Box 4.2.

Multistate life table method

Multistate life tables yield measures of health expectancy based on movements between health states; that is, transitions. The health expectancies may be for the whole population of a particular age (population based), or for those in a given health state at that age (status based). The method therefore makes it possible to compare health expectancies for those in different health states and to show the rates of moving between states during a specified time interval. The

Figure 4.2: Average life expectancy at birth

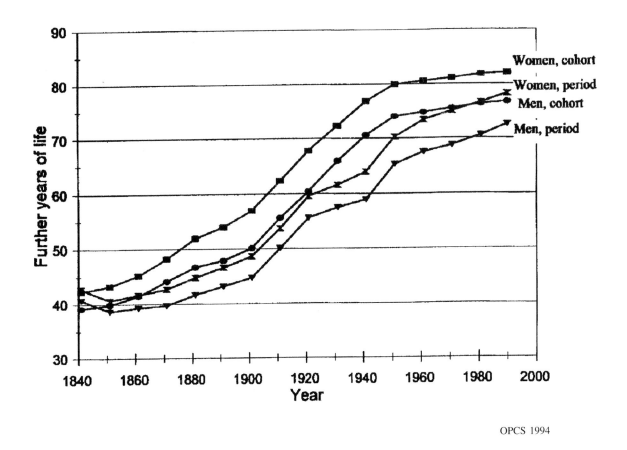

OPCS 1994

rates at which people acquire various kinds and levels of disability, and the time they spend in these health states before improving or dying determines their need for different health and social services. It is because they yield both more accurate and richer information that multistate life tables provide a better basis than the Sullivan method for predicting service needs and for estimating the effects of particular interventions. In addition, the transition probabilities allow the prediction of the life-time risk to individuals of particular states of ill-health (Bebbington, 1992), and projections of the future health state of the population, and so of related health and social service needs. The method of calculation is outlined in more detail in chapter 11, where it is applied to UK data.

As noted earlier, multistate life tables may be used to derive health expectancies for a population at a particular period, or for real cohorts.

The information needed to calculate health expectancy by the multistate method is:

- the health/disability/dependency status of individuals in a population at successive time points from which the intervening transition rates can be calculated;

- information about deaths among those individuals during the period of observation.

The data can be obtained from a longitudinal sample survey or recording system of the relevant population (e.g. those aged 65 or over) in which data for those initially included are recorded over time. This is considered further in the final chapters of this report.

The multistate method of calculating health expectancy is preferable for most purposes, given the probability, discussed in chapter 3, that transition rates have not been stable in recent times. Box 4.3 summarises the calculation methods appropriate for different policy applications.

Box 4.3: Health expectancy calculation methods appropriate for different policy purposes

Policy application	Appropriate method	Source data needed
1 Health trend monitoring	Sullivan's	cross-sectional (if transition rates have been stable) (repeated) longitudinal
2 Population comparison (equity/risk identification)	Sullivan's	cross-sectional
3 Health outcomes of intervention strategies	Multistate current cohort	longitudinal two-wave multi-wave/continuing
4 Service planning short term (5-10 yrs)	Sullivan's	cross-sectional
long term (up to 25+yrs)	Multistate current cohort	longitudinal two-wave multi-wave/continuing

5 Comparisons and comparability of health expectancy measures/values

Comparison of health outcomes in different countries is one of the starting points for unravelling contributory factors. Comparisons within a country over time are needed for monitoring trends and may also help to identify the effects of particular factors. In this chapter we compare health expectancies in this country with comparable others, and show trends over time. We then describe existing obstacles to comparability so as to indicate how they might be overcome in the future.

5.1 Comparison between countries

Health expectancies can only be comparable if they are based on the same definitions of health and morbidity. There are no exactly comparable health expectancy figures for this and any other country in this sense. There are, however, a small number of countries in which it appears that the measure of disability from which health expectancy values were derived resembled that of the OPCS Surveys of Disability used by Bebbington (1992): in particular, the questionnaires show that the prevalence data were yielded by questions about a range of specified disabilities, even though they were combined in different ways, and the threshold of disability and of severe disability are differently determined. All the population surveys which produced the disability data covered both private households and institutions, and in all cases health expectancies were calculated by the Sullivan method. The methods of the Canadian HALS survey were probably the most similar to the British surveys, and those of the French survey least so.

Comparisons are shown in Table 5.1. Despite some differences in definition of disability, the values for disability-free life expectancy and for severe disability-free life expectancy at birth, and for each as a proportion of total life expectancy appear to be quite similar. So, for example, boys born in Britain in 1985 could on average expect nearly 72 years of life, of which nearly 64 years (89%) would be without disability and 70 years (over 97%) without severe disability. In Canada, boys born a year later, in 1986, could look forward to 73 years of life, of which just over 61 years (84%) would be disability free, and 72 years (over 98%) would be without severe disability.

It seems, then, that disability-free life expectancy in Britain is in line with that in other similar countries.

5.2 Comparisons over time: is there a compression of morbidity?

International evidence

Several countries have now produced disability-free life expectancy figures for more than one time point. These have been assembled and reviewed by Robine and Ritchie (Robine and Ritchie, 1993). Within each country included the same definition of morbidity has been used on each occasion, but definitions vary between countries. The results for females are shown in Figure 5.1. With the exception of that for France, the trends indicate an expansion of morbidity: whereas life expectancy has increased by about 6 years over a 25 year period, disability-free life expectancy at birth has remained around 63 years. Thus the years of life expectancy gained appear to be years of disability.

Some of the countries included in the series have monitored life expectancy free of different levels of disability. Trends in three countries in very severe disability (defined as: unable to live outside an institution and/or bed-ridden) are shown in Figure 5.2. They suggest that these are running parallel with trends in life expectancy, and so indicate a relative compression of morbidity of this kind (because years of life spent with very severe disability form a decreasing proportion of total years of life over time).

It seems from this evidence, as Robine and Ritchie conclude, that the aging of the population is currently being accompanied by a pandemic of light to moderate disability, but a compression of disability of the more severe levels. The evidence, however, may be misleading. First, as discussed in chapter 4, health expectancy calculated by the Sullivan method may fail to capture changes in the health status of a population as they occur; second, the equating of residence in institutions with a particular level of disability will confound trends if the proportion or kind of people in institutions is changing.

Evidence for this country

The trend for this country is represented in Figure 5.1 by health expectancies calculated from answers to the General Household Survey questions on limiting long-standing illness, combined with estimates for residents of institutions (Bebbington, 1991). This has hitherto been the only existing time series of health expectancies here. The figures, updated to 1992, are given in detail in chapter 6 and are summarised in Table 5.2. They show, as was seen in Figure 5.1, fluctuations in disability-free life expectancy (DFLE) over the years covered since 1976, but, although for both men and women the expected years of life without disability were about one year greater in 1992 than in 1976, there is no clear trend. Life expectancy increased steadily over the same period (by about three years at birth and by about one year for people aged 65), but disability-free life expectancy as a *percentage* of life expectancy fluctuated over the period: except for women aged 65, the percentage was slightly lower in 1992 than in 1976. Thus, the trend in the ratio of health expectancy

Table 5.1: Disability-free life expectancy (DFLE) and severe disability-free life expectancy (SDFLE) at birth, based on questions about specific disabilities: comparison of five countries

	GB	Australia		Canada	France	
	1985	1981	1988	1986	1981	1991
Males	*years*					
LE*	71.7	71.4	73.1	73.0	70.4	72.9
DFLE**	63.6	59.2	58.4	61.3	60.8	63.8
SDFLE***	70.0	68.5	69.9	72.0	68.9	71.7
	percent					
DFLE/LE	88.7	82.9	79.9	84.0	86.4	87.5
SDFLE/LE	97.6	95.9	95.6	98.6	97.9	98.4
Females	*years*					
LE*	77.5	78.4	79.5	79.8	78.6	81.1
DFLE**	66.5	65.0	63.4	64.9	65.9	68.5
SDFLE***	74.5	73.2	73.5	77.8	76.3	78.8
	percent					
DFLE/LE	85.8	82.9	79.7	81.3	83.8	84.5
SDFLE/LE	96.1	93.4	92.5	97.5	97.1	97.2

 *LE = life expectancy
 **DFLE = disability-free life expectancy
***SDFLE = severe disability-free life expectancy

Sources
1   Health expectancy calculations

     Great Britain - Bebbington, 1992.
     Australia - Mathers, 1991.
     Canada - Wilkins and Adams, 1992.
     France - Robine and Mormiche, 1993.

2   Disability prevalence

     Great Britain - OPCS Surveys of Disability in Great Britain. (Severe disability defined as severity level 7 to 10)
     Australia - Australian Bureau of Statistics population surveys
     Canada - Statistics Canada, The Health and Activity Limitation Survey
     France - INSEE (Institut National de la Statistique et de Etudes Economiques), Enquete sur la sante et les soins medicaux.

Table 5.2: Expectation of life without limiting long-standing illness in England and Wales, 1976-1991

Year	at 0-4 years			at 65-74 years		
	LE*	HE**	HE/LE	LE*	HE**	HE/LE
	yrs	*yrs*	*%*		*yrs*	*%*
Males						
1976	70.0	58.3	83	12.5	7.1	57
1981	71.1	58.7	83	13.1	7.9	60
1985	71.9	58.8	82	13.4	7.8	58
1988	72.4	58.5	81	13.7	7.5	55
1991	73.2	59.9	82	14.2	7.9	56
Females						
1976	76.1	62.0	81	16.6	8.6	52
1981	77.1	61.0	79	17.1	8.5	50
1985	77.7	61.9	80	17.3	9.2	53
1988	78.1	61.2	78	17.6	8.7	50
1991	78.7	63.0	80	17.9	9.8	55

 *LE = life expectancy
**HE = health expectancy (here, expectation of life without limiting long-standing illness).

Figure 5.1: Change in life expectancy and disability-free life expectancy (moderate), females at birth. United States, United Kingdom, Australia, Netherlands, 1964-1988

From Robine and Ritchie, 1993.

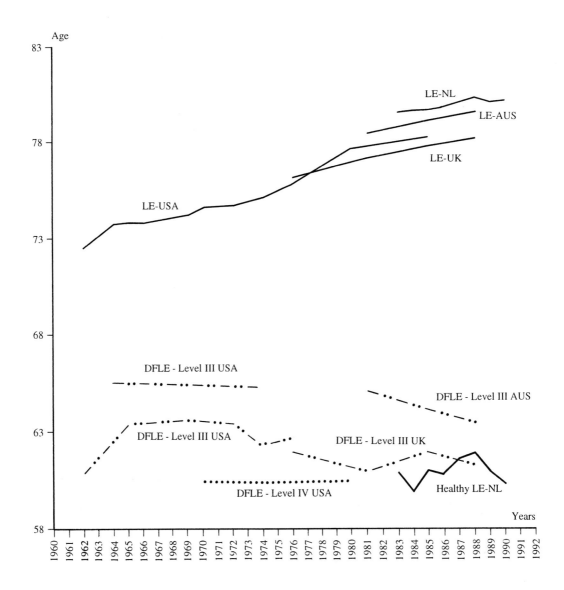

Disability - free life expectancy Level III and IV, Females at birth
Healthy life expectancies in the Netherlands, 1983-1990

Levels of disability severity

I.   *Very severe disability = unable to live outside an institution (long-term) and/or bedridden.*

II.   *Severe to very severe disability = level I plus those totally giving up principal activity (long term).*

III. *Moderate to very severe disability = levels I and II plus those having a long-term limitation in their ability to carry out any activity (whether principal activity or other).*

IV. *Mild to very severe disability = levels I, II and III plus short-term disability.*

Figure 5.2: **Change in life expectancy and disability-free life expectancy (very severe), females at birth. United States, Japan, France, 1964-1991**

From Robine and Ritchie, 1993.

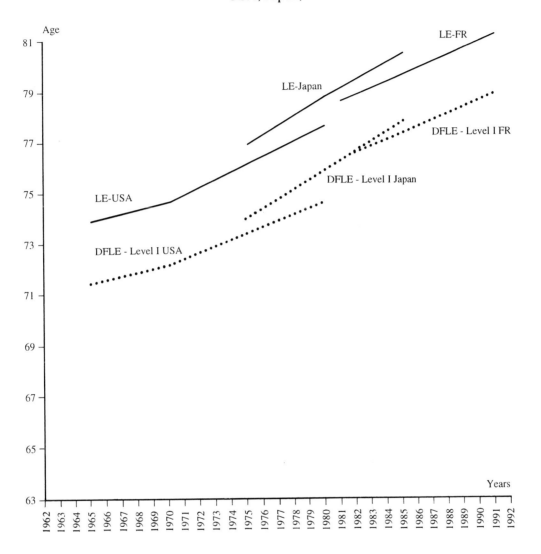

Disability - free life expectancy Level I, Females at birth
USA, Japan, France

Levels of disability severity

I.   *Very severe disability = unable to live outside an institution (long-term) and/or bedridden.*

II. *Severe to very severe disability = level I plus those totally giving up principal activity (long term).*

III. *Moderate to very severe disability = levels I and II plus those having a long-term limitation in their ability to carry out any activity (whether principal activity or other).*

IV. *Mild to very severe disability = levels I, II and III plus short-term disability.*

17

to life expectancy - where health expectancy has been based on the GHS question on limiting long-standing illness - indicates no compression of morbidity.

The trend in health expectancy calculated from questions on the ability to perform activities of daily living without help (ADLs) presents a different picture. Table 5.3 gives figures extracted from a new time series of ADL-based health expectancies for older people which are shown in detail in chapter 6. Inability to perform ADLs represents a severe level of disability, and the figures indicate, like those for the US, Japan and France, a compression of this type of morbidity.

5.3 Existing obstacles to comparability

Figure 5.3 shows health expectancy in fourteen OECD countries, collected by REVES (Réseau Esperance de Vie en Santé - The International Network on health expectancy) and most recently published by the OECD (OECD, 1993). It illustrates immediately one of the obstacles to comparability; namely, differences in the reference population. Whereas for most of the countries, health expectancy is calculated from birth, for Denmark, New Zealand and Sweden it is calculated for only for part of the life span. Moreover, figures for Japan and New Zealand are for both sexes combined, whereas other countries give figures for each sex separately.

For the 10 countries which appear to be comparable in these respects (although note that the calendar years differ) health expectancy varies more than life expectancy - by more than ten years compared with under five: health expectancy varies from 60 to 73 years in the case of females, and from 56 to 67 years for males. Life expectancy, on the other hand, varies from 78 to 81 years for females, and from 70 to 74 years for males. The UK appears to have one of the shortest periods of health expectancy, just over 61 years for females and just over 58 for males, compared with the longest periods of 73 and 67 years, respectively, in Switzerland. So, on the basis of the table, it might be assumed that had Swiss conditions prevailed in the UK, women here (for example) might on average expect to enjoy an extra 12 years of good health - but only 2 or 3 extra years of life.

The assumption would not be justified by this evidence. Few if any of the health expectancy figures shown are likely to be exactly comparable with one another, although all were calculated using the Sullivan method; most notably the concept of ill-health varies, and in particular the questions asked to identify it differ. Thus, for example, the Swiss questions (which concerned disability) excluded any on all but the most extreme form of locomotor disability (Boshuizen and van de Water, 1994), which may account for the unusually high health expectancy value shown for Switzerland.

In general, the methods for calculating health expectancy are widely agreed, and the differences between them understood, largely as a result of the work of REVES. Instead, the main impediments to comparability lie in differences in the data to which the methods are applied. The main differences occur in:

- the concept and operational definition of ill-health used as a basis for the calculations (including whether only chronic conditions are included);

- the population to which the data refer (particularly whether the institutional population is included);

- other aspects of the system by which the data on ill-health are collected and produced.

In what follows we consider each of these in turn, partly to indicate the factors which currently hinder comparisons, but - more importantly - to identify the requirements for improving comparability in the future.

The concept and definition of ill-health used

An example of the effect of using different definitions is illustrated by Table 5.4. It shows health expectancies at birth in 1985 as calculated by using two different sources of data on ill health: the General Household Survey (GHS), and the OPCS Surveys of Disability (Martin et al, 1988; Bone and Meltzer, 1989). In both cases the Sullivan method was used to estimate health expectancy. The institutional population is included in the calculations. However, whereas the health status of those in institutions was obtained by interview, for the Disability Surveys the health status of the institutional population was estimated for the GHS figures.

It can be seen that health expectancy derived from the Disability Surveys was some 4 years more, for both males and females, than that based on the GHS. Had the former been used in the OECD table, health expectancy for the UK would have been in the middle of the range rather than one of the lowest. Moreover, if change in health expectancy in this country were to be assessed by comparing the value derived from one of these sources on the first occasion and from the other on the second, a quite spurious indication of a compression or expansion of morbidity would result.

The differences are due to the different sets of questions used on the two surveys to identify disability[1]. The GHS asks about limiting long-standing illness, whereas the Disability Surveys asked detailed questions about specific disabilities of all kinds, but imposed a threshold on the activity limitation which defined it as a disability. The resulting differences in both the overall and age specific prevalence of disability are illustrated in Figure 5.4. The GHS age-specific prevalence figures are represented by the black circles, the Disability Survey figures by black triangles. (The Census figures are discussed later.) In 1985, the GHS showed 20% of the private household population aged 16 or over to have a limiting long-standing illness, whereas only 13% were identified as having a disability according to the Disability Surveys. Not only the difference in prevalence but also the way disability is related to age will affect estimates of health expectancy.

---

[1] Figures derived from the GHS relate to England and Wales, whereas those from the Disability Surveys are for Great Britain. However, as life expectancy for Scotland is slightly lower than for England and Wales, and the prevalence of disability in Scotland differs little from that of Great Britain according to the OPCS Disability Surveys, the difference between the two sets of health expectancy figures cannot be due to the difference in the populations covered.

Figure 5.3: Life expectancy in good health, by country (in years) (OECD, 1993)

		Australia	Austria	Belguim	Canada	Denmark	Finland	France	Germany
YEAR		1981	..	..	1951	..	..	..	..
Life expectancy female		78.4	..	..	70.8	..	..	..	..
Disability-free life expectancy		65.0	..	..	64.7	..	..	..	..
Ratio Disability-free life/Female life expectancy		82.9	..	..	91.4	..	..	..	..
Life expectancy male		71.4	..	..	66.3	..	..	..	..
Disability-free life expectancy		59.2	..	..	59.8	..	..	..	..
Ratio Disability-free life/Male life expectancy		82.9	..	..	90.2	..	..	..	..
YEAR		1988	..	..	1978	1986	..	1982	1986
Life expectancy female		79.5	..	..	78.3	62.4	..	78.9	78.4
Disability-free life expectancy		63.4	..	..	66.1	57.1	..	67.1	68.4
Ratio Disability-free life/Female life expectancy		79.7	..	..	84.4	91.5	..	85.0	87.2
Life expectancy male		73.1	..	..	70.8	56.7	..	70.7	71.8
Disability-free life expectancy		58.4	..	..	61.1	53.0	..	61.9	63.4
Ratio Disability-free life/Male life expectancy		79.9	..	..	86.3	93.5	..	87.6	88.3

	Greece	Iceland	Ireland	Italy	Japan	Luxem-borg	Nether-lands	New Zealand
YEAR	..	..	..	1980	1966	..	1981	..
Life expectancy female	..	..	..	77 4	70 9	..	79 3	..
Disability-free life expectancy	..	..	..	63.9	68.1	..	58.0	..
Ratio Disability-free life/Female life expectancy	..	..	..	82.6	96.1	..	73.1	..
Life expectancy male	..	..	..	70.6	..	..	72.7	..
Disability-free life expectancy	..	..	..	60.6	..	..	56.9	..
Ratio Disability-free life/Male life expectancy	..	..	..	85.8	..	..	78.3	..
YEAR	..	..	..	1983	1970	..	1990	1984
Life expectancy female	..	..	..	78.2	71.9	..	80.1	47.4
Disability-free life expectancy	..	..	..	68.3	68.8	..	60.2	41.4
Ratio Disability-free life/Female life expectancy	..	..	..	87.3	95.6	..	75.1	87.3
Life expectancy male	..	..	..	71.6	..	..	73.9	..
Disability-free life expectancy	..	..	..	64.3	..	..	60.0	..
Ratio Disability-free life/Male life expectancy	..	..	..	89.8	..	..	81.2	..

	Norway	Portugal	Spain	Sweden	Switzerland	Turkey	United Kingdom	United States
YEAR	1981	..	..	1951	..	..	..	..
Life expectancy female	78.4	..	..	70.8	..	..	..	..
Disability-free life expectancy	65.0	..	..	64.7	..	..	..	..
Ratio Disability-free life/Female life expectancy	82.9	..	..	91.4	..	..	..	..
Life expectancy male	71.4	..	..	66.3	..	..	..	..
Disability-free life expectancy	59.2	..	..	59.8	..	..	..	..
Ratio Disability-free life/Male life expectancy	82.9	..	..	90.2	..	..	..	..
YEAR	1988	..	..	1978	1986	..	1982	1986
Life expectancy female	79.5	..	..	78.3	62.4	..	78.9	78.4
Disability-free life expectancy	63.4	..	..	66.1	57.1	..	67.1	68.4
Ratio Disability-free life/Female life expectancy	79.7	..	..	84.4	91.5	..	85.0	87.2
Life expectancy male	73.1	..	..	70.8	56.7	..	70.7	71.8
Disability-free life expectancy	58.4	..	..	61.1	53.0	..	61.9	63.4
Ratio Disability-free life/Male life expectancy	79.9	..	..	86.3	93.5	..	87.6	88.3

Courtesy REVES, International Network for the study of Healthy Life Expectancy.
1. The underlying disability-free concepts are not fully homogeneous across countries and over time.
2. The Japanese and New Zealand entries refer to both sexes, not only to females.
3. The Danish entries refer to life expectancy at age 16. The New Zealand entries to the 15-64 life-span, the Swedish entries to the 16-64 life-span.

Table 5.3: Expectation of life without inability to perform activities of daily living (ADLs) at age 65-69. Great Britain, 1976 to 1991

Year	Males			Females		
	LE* yrs	HE** yrs	HE/LE %	LE* yrs	HE** yrs	HE/LE %
1976	12.5	11.0	88	16.5	13.0	79
1980	12.9	11.8	91	16.9	15.0	89
1985	13.4	12.3	92	17.4	15.5	89
1991	14.3	13.6	95	18.1	16.9	93

*LE = life expectancy
**HE = health expectancy

Table 5.4: Health expectancies at birth in 1985. Comparison of those calculated from the GHS limiting long-standing illness questions with those calculated from the OPCS Disability Surveys

Males				Females			
GHS (E&W)		Disability Surveys (GB)		GHS (E&W)		Disability Surveys (GB)	
LE* yrs	HE** yrs	LE* yrs	HE** yrs	LE* yrs	HE** yrs	LE* yrs	HE** yrs
71.9	58.8	71.7	63.6	77.7	61.9	77.5	66.5

*LE = life expectancy
**HE = health expectancy

Table 5.5: Health expectancy - Effect of differing age-specific disability prevalence, given a constant overall disability prevalence

e.g. Health expectancy (HE) derived from GHS limiting long-standing illness question using
    (a)   1985 GHS prevalence data and
    (b)   data based on GHS overall disability prevalence but shaped like curve from Disability Surveys

Age	Original GHS LLI rates (per 1000)	HE derived from original GHS LLI rates	Adjusted LLI rates (per 1000)	HE derived from adjusted LLI rates	Difference between the two HE measures
16-19	78	46.01	94	46.07	- 0.06
20-24	76	41.56	100	41.70	- 0.14
25-29	90	37.09	104	37.35	- 0.26
30-34	105	32.69	113	33.03	- 0.34
35-39	127	28.37	117	28.75	- 0.38
40-44	144	24.14	132	24.47	- 0.33
45-49	172	20.15	152	20.42	- 0.27
50-54	223	16.34	179	16.52	- 0.18
55-59	296	12.97	228	12.93	0.04
60-64	345	10.12	278	9.73	0.39
65-69	369	7.80	348	7.00	0.80
70-74	391	5.78	415	4.71	1.07
75-79	449	4.14	539	2.87	1.27
80-84	477	2.89	689	1.50	1.39
85+	588	1.81	852	0.65	1.16

If overall prevalence were 20% as shown by the GHS in 1985, but the distribution by age followed a similar curve to that of disability from the Disability Surveys as shown in Figure 5.5, health expectancies at each age would differ, as shown in Table 5.5. For example, at ages 35 the adjusted figures yield over 4.5 more months of life in good health than the actual GHS data, whereas from age 70 the adjusted figures lead to over one year less of good health.

The questions used on the GHS and on the Disability Surveys to identify disability were very different, but much smaller variations can also affect results. Thus a question on limiting long-standing illness similar to, but slightly different from, the GHS version was employed on the 1991 Census. The questions were:

GHS   *Do you have any long-standing illness, disability or infirmity?*
       Does this illness or disability limit your activities in any way?

Census *Does the person have any long term illness, health problem or handicap which limits his/her daily activities or the work he/she can do? Include problems which are due to old age.*

The resulting difference in overall prevalence is as great as that between the GHS and Disability Surveys; the GHS for 1991 showed 18% of the private household population of all ages to have a limiting long-standing illness, whereas the Census showed only 12% to be affected. The age specific prevalence patterns also differ as Figure 5.4 shows. The Census figures for the total population of England and Wales are represented by stars, and those for the private household population by the line without symbols. It can be seen that the Census figures describe a curve which more closely resembles the results of the Disability Surveys than those of the GHS of 1985[2]. Later in this report health expectancies based on both the Census and GHS questions are given: they differ by about 4 years.

A further problem occurs because some health expectancy measures, unlike those which have been produced in this country, include limiting *short*-term disability, e.g. Canada 1986 (Wilkins, 1992), US 1980 (Crimmins et al, 1992), Netherlands 1981-5 (van Ginneken et al, 1992). In these cases the expected number of years of life with short-term disability is not always shown separately, so that comparison with measures confined to long-term disability cannot be made.

Reference population

The problem of comparing health expectancies where different age spans are covered was apparent from the earlier OECD table, and the difficulty of comparing figures for different combinations of constituent parts of the same country was evident in the case of Great Britain versus England and Wales figures. Less obvious, however, and at least as damaging to comparisons, is any omission of the institutional population.

Although residents of institutions usually form only a tiny proportion of the total population, they are not a negligible proportion of either the very old or of those with disabilities: the 1991 Census shows only 1.3% of the total population of Great Britain to be resident in communal establishments, compared with over 7% of those with limiting long-term illness, nearly one quarter of the population aged 85 or more, and almost one third of this older group with a limiting long-term illness. The divergence with age of the total and private household population can be seen in Figure 5.4.

The proportion of the population in institutions differs from one country to another, and changes within the same country from time to time - for example, as a result of policies favouring care in the community rather than in long stay institutions. Comparability therefore requires the inclusion of the population in institutions. Because some sources of morbidity data, like the GHS, relate only to the private household population, the health/disability status of those in institutions must be estimated to produce health expectancy figures by the Sullivan method - as was done for the GHS based health expectancy figures shown earlier, and those presented later in this report. It is common to assume that all those in institutions (or, some constant proportion of them) suffer from the particular form of morbidity or disability of interest. This in itself impairs comparisons between countries and over time, unless there is other evidence of any change, or absence of change, in the health status of the institutional population which can be used to inform the estimates. For example, a policy favouring care in the community might be expected to change the composition of the population in communal establishments over time so that a greater proportion than before implementation of the policy were severely disabled. Thus only enquiries which cover people in communal establishments, like the Census and OPCS Disability Surveys, provide an unquestionably firm basis - particularly for the elderly - for estimating change over time.

For the multistate lifetable method, residents of institutions must be included from the beginning of the study, and those in private households at the outset who subsequently enter institutions must be followed up.

Other aspects of the system of data collection and production

Other aspects of the way data are collected, recorded and edited may also affect comparability. In the first case, for example: whether data are collected by face to face interview, or telephone; whether interviews are conducted by professional interviewers or health service personnel; and whether or not proxies are used for sample members who find it difficult or impossible to answer on their own behalf (which reduces any non-response bias) may all affect the outcome, and therefore comparability with data collected

---

[2]Answers to questions on limiting long-term illness appear to be particularly sensitive to questions wording. The evidence of the difference between prevalence rates yielded by the GHS and the 1991 Census, is supplemented by that of the 1987 Quebec Health Survey, which asked: 'Compared to other (persons) of the same age, is -- limited in kind or amount of activity he/she can do because of a long-term physical or mental condition or health problem?' This yielded a prevalence rate of just over 7% (Wilkins, 1992a). It seems unlikely that health in Quebec is so much better than in this country.

Figure 5.4: Limiting long-standing illness from 1991 Census compared with GHS 1985 and OPCS Disability Surveys 1985

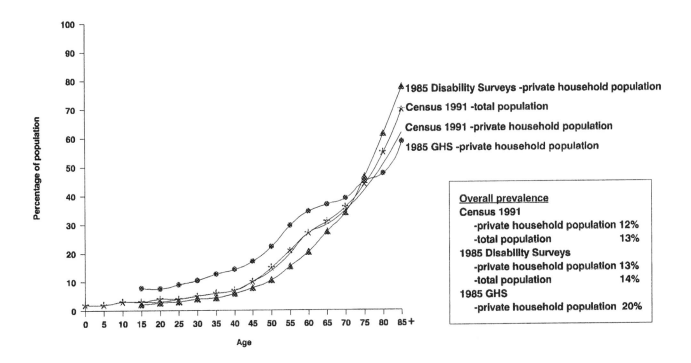

Figure 5.5: Adjusting the GHS estimate of health expectancy to reflect the age distribution of disability prevalence in the Disability Survey

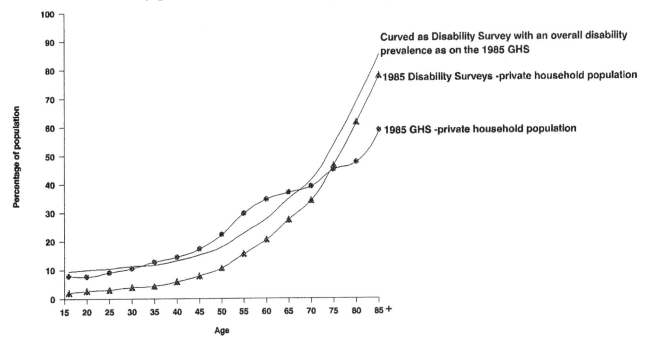

differently. Differences in the editing of identical questions - eg, the way in which 'No answers' are treated or coding categories combined - may also impair comparability. Thus, for example, it has been shown for the Netherlands that a time series of healthy life expectancy derived from pre-coded answers to a self-perceived health question (asked over a period of 8 years, from 1983 to 1990) indicate either an improvement or deterioration over time according to the way the coding categories are combined (Boshuizen, 1993). More generally, even where exactly the same question or questions (e.g. on activities of daily living - ADLs) are asked at different times or in different places, the particular way the answers are treated or combined in each study will affect comparability.

All of these factors apply to both cross-sectional and longitudinal data, but in addition, in the case of longitudinal surveys which yield material for the multistate life table method, one of the factors affecting comparability will be the time period between waves of data capture. Because transitions are normally inferred from observed changes in state between one wave and the next, other things being equal, a study with a short interval between waves will identify more transitions per unit of time than one with a longer interval. Moreover, as the chances of becoming disabled increase with advancing age, and if it is common for a final period of chronic disability to be preceded by shorter episodes of disability, then a longer interval between waves of a longitudinal study means that it is more likely than one with a shorter interval to capture only transitions from health to disability, and to miss recoveries and remissions. A means of estimating the optimal time between waves has been proposed by Brouard (Brouard, 1994).

Summary of requirements for comparability

In summary, the main requirements for comparability of health expectancy measures are that, for all populations or time points to be compared:

- the concept of disability and questions used to elicit the source data should be virtually identical;

- disability prevalence data for the institutional population, as well as that of private households, should be included;

- the mode of administering the measurement instruments and of combining the raw source data should be the same;

- for longitudinal data, the intervals between data collection waves should be the same.

In addition, the more specific and objective the questions on morbidity/disability are, the less the prevalence data are likely to be affected by cultural and temporal variations in expectations and interpretations.

6 Calculation of trends in health expectancies, 1976-1992

In this chapter we compare, for this country, the trends in health expectancy based on limiting long-standing illness (LLI) with that based on the more severe levels of disability represented by inability to perform the basic activities of daily living (ADLs).

6.1 Calculation of trends in health expectancy using the limiting long-standing illness question from the General Household Survey, 1976-1992

This section extends previous calculations of trends in health expectancy based on the General Household Survey (Bebbington, 1991); to include data for 1991 and 1992. The analytical method (Sullivan's method) is identical to that described in chapter 4 and will not be repeated here. The purpose of continuing this analysis is to examine whether increases in life expectancy are being matched by corresponding improvements in morbidity. This is relevant to predictions of the future demand for long-term care as the population ages.

The evidence is taken from the GHS question concerning limiting long-standing illness, which is counted as present if there are answers of 'yes' to both of the following:

- *Do you have any long-standing illness, disability or infirmity?*
- *Does this illness or disability limit your activities in any way?*

The published figures from the GHS apply to Great Britain as a whole but for the present purposes are assumed to apply equally to England and Wales. These rates are shown in Table 6.1 (by age group and sex), for the years 1976, 1981, 1985, 1988, 1991 and 1992; together with the sample sizes on which they were based. However, the GHS does not include people not living in private households: those living in hostels, nursing homes and similar. In the previously published analysis the numbers of disabled people not living in private households were estimated from the number of people present in particular types of institution serving the chronically ill. However, with changes in the annual returns from such institutions, it has become increasingly difficult to sustain this series broken down by age and sex as required.

As an alternative, estimates of the disabled population not in private households have been prepared from the national censuses of 1971, 1981 and 1991, applying the limiting long-standing illness rates from the 1991 census for such people. Figures for the numbers of people not present in private households were 1.44m in 1971; 1.21m in 1981 and 1.37m in 1991. These figures are comparable, but include all people enumerated outside private households whether normally resident in private households or no. (In 1991, 55 per cent of those enumerated were residents of communal establishments). These numbers are available by age group

and sex. The figures shown in Table 6.1 are the actual numbers for 1981 and 1991 (extrapolated to 1992), and are constructed by linear interpolation between censuses for the other years. The rate of limiting long-standing illness among people enumerated outside private households by age and sex is calculated from the number of people with LLI.

What in effect is being assumed, is that at each point in time all people currently in communal establishments experience the age/sex specific LLI rates current at the time of the 1991 Census (Table 6.2) while all the remainder, those in private households, experience the age/sex LLI rates corresponding to the current GHS. This assumption is fairly rough and ready. In particular, it is doubtful that LLI rates in communal establishments have remained stationary over 15 years (though figures presented by Darton and Wright (1993) imply that the change has been less than is often assumed). Nevertheless, they are made tenable for the purpose of estimating overall LLI rates because the estimated number of disabled people in private households greatly outnumbers those in communal establishments. The consequence is that estimates of overall rates are fairly robust to assumptions about non-private households. For example, if the overall LLI rates in Table 6.1 are compared with those in Table 2 of Bebbington (1991), it will be seen that the completely different treatment of non-private households rarely makes more than a very slight difference.

With these assumptions in mind, Table 6.1 shows the life expectancy, age-specific LLI rate, and healthy life expectancy at various ages, for men and women in 1976, 1981, 1985, 1988, 1991, and 1992. In 1992 for instance, healthy life expectancy at birth was 59.7 years for men and 61.9 years for women.

Our main conclusions concern trends. Figures 6.1 and 6.2 show life expectancies and health expectancies between 1976 and 1992, at birth and at age 65. Since 1976 there has been a continuing rise in overall life expectancies for both men and women, equivalent to a gain of about 3 months per annum. In contrast, health expectancy remained almost constant between 1976 and 1988, at about 58.5 years for men and 61.5 for women. There may have been a slight upturn in 1991 and 1992, most noticeably for men at birth.

The consequence is that overall there has been a relentless increase in the expectation of unhealthy life. For men it rose from 11.7 years in 1976 to 14.0 years in 1992; for women the corresponding increase was from 14.1 to 17.3 years. This seems to support the pessimistic view that we are likely to experience an expansion of morbidity and a consequent increased demand for health and social services as the population continues to age. However, the GHS limiting long-standing illness question does include comparatively mild conditions. We shall now examine evidence about severer forms of disability that suggest the situation is not necessarily so unpromising.

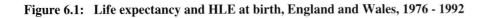

Figure 6.1: Life expectancy and HLE at birth, England and Wales, 1976 - 1992

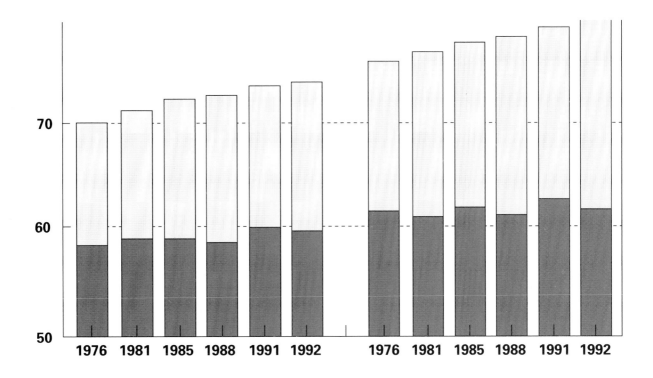

Males and Females

Figure 6.2: Life expectancy and HLE at age 65, England and Wales, 1976 - 1992

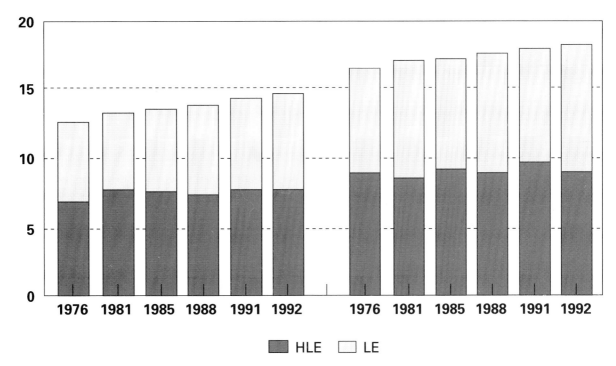

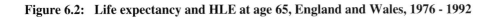

Males and Females

Table 6.1: Healthy life expectancy (HLE) calculated from General Household Survey, 1976-1991

	Pop. (thou)	I(0)	Life expect	GHS LLI rate	GHS n	Comm pop	Comm LLI	All LLI (thou)	d(x)	LWD(x)	HLE(x)	Ratio
1976												
Men												
0 - 4	1,658	10,000	70.0	2.2	905	15,600	9.1	37.6	2.3	48,020	58.3	83
5 - 14	4,091	9,817	66.3	6.0	1,976	56,900	9.1	247.2	6.0	92,038	54.5	82
15 - 44	9,985	9,786	56.5	9.0	5,121	372,500	14.4	918.8	9.2	262,772	45.3	80
45 - 64	5,583	9,411	28.0	24.9	2,666	117,900	46.1	1,415.2	25.3	129,266	19.2	69
65 - 74	1,963	7,228	12.5	37.9	965	52,600	72.0	761.9	38.8	35,885	7.1	57
75+	809	4,284	7.4	48.4	519	60,000	88.0	415.3	51.3	15,427	3.6	49
Women												
0 - 4	1,569	10,000	76.1	1.7	811	13,700	8.8	27.6	1.8	48,385	62.0	81
5 - 14	3,876	9,858	72.2	4.7	1,833	35,200	9.1	183.7	4.7	93,277	58.0	80
15 - 44	9,678	9,837	62.4	8.8	5,229	236,800	12.8	861.1	8.9	267,010	48.6	78
45 - 64	5,901	9,603	33.4	23.0	2,844	98,800	44.5	1,378.5	23.4	139,852	22.0	66
65 - 74	2,577	8,329	16.6	40.0	1,213	70,300	74.7	1,055.2	40.9	44,610	8.6	52
75+	1,769	6,400	9.8	52.9	963	194,100	92.5	1,012.7	57.2	26,816	4.2	43
1981												
Men												
0 - 4	1,542	10,000	71.1	3.0	882	12,000	9.1	47.0	3.0	48,344	58.7	83
5 - 14	3,639	9,853	67.1	8.0	1,898	42,100	9.1	291.6	8.0	90,245	54.7	81
15 - 44	10,603	9,826	57.3	10.0	4,975	336,900	14.4	1,075.1	10.1	261,452	45.7	80
45 - 64	5,405	9,480	28.7	26.0	2,707	99,900	46.1	1,425.4	26.4	128,699	19.7	69
65 - 74	2,020	7,426	13.1	35.0	1,040	48,900	72.0	725.1	35.9	39,330	7.9	60
75+	951	4,606	7.8	44.0	585	61,800	88.0	445.6	46.9	19,092	4.1	53
Women												
0 - 4	1,464	10,000	77.1	3.0	802	10,600	8.8	44.5	3.0	47,892	61.0	79
5 - 14	3,446	9,885	73.0	6.0	1,800	28,300	9.1	207.6	6.0	93,092	56.8	78
15 - 44	10,351	9,866	63.1	11.0	5,233	213,700	12.8	1,142.5	11.0	260,815	47.5	75
45 - 64	5,635	9,659	34.1	26.0	2,800	79,000	44.5	1,479.7	26.3	136,481	21.5	63
65 - 74	2,599	8,438	17.1	41.0	1,289	62,800	74.7	1,086.8	41.8	44,090	8.5	50
75+	1,979	6,588	10.4	56.0	1,087	211,000	92.5	1,185.3	59.9	27,480	4.2	40
1985												
Men												
0 - 4	1,615	10,000	71.9	4.0	905	12,100	9.1	65.2	4.0	47,477	58.8	82
5 - 14	3,262	9,875	67.8	8.0	1,976	44,500	9.1	261.4	8.0	90,299	54.8	81
15 - 44	11,019	9,851	58.0	10.0	5,121	344,400	14.4	1,117.1	10.1	261,790	45.8	79
45 - 64	5,421	9,525	29.4	27.0	2,666	94,900	46.1	1,481.8	27.3	129,331	19.8	67
65 - 74	1,934	7,616	13.4	38.0	965	49,200	72.0	751.6	38.9	38,641	7.8	58
75+	1,079	4,856	8.0	43.0	519	75,000	88.0	497.7	46.1	20,928	4.3	54
Women												
0 - 4	1,536	10,000	77.7	3.0	811	10,400	8.8	46.7	3.0	47,708	61.9	80
5 - 14	3,086	9,902	73.5	6.0	1,833	29,300	9.1	186.1	6.0	93,135	57.7	78
15 - 44	10,764	9,885	63.6	11.0	5,229	224,100	12.8	1,188.1	11.0	262,598	48.3	76
45 - 64	5,586	9,695	34.4	26.0	2,844	73,900	44.5	1,466.0	26.2	137,050	22.2	65
65 - 74	2,461	8,537	17.3	38.0	1,213	62,100	74.7	958.0	38.9	47,126	9.2	53
75+	2,159	6,717	10.5	51.0	963	253,400	92.5	1,206.3	55.9	31,124	4.6	44
1988												
Men												
0 - 4	1,684	10,000	72.4	4.0	882	12,100	9.1	68.0	4.0	47,407	58.5	81
5 - 14	3,144	9,877	68.3	9.0	1,898	46,300	9.1	283.0	9.0	90,203	54.4	80
15 - 44	11,245	9,854	58.4	11.0	4,975	350,000	14.4	1,248.9	11.1	259,108	45.4	78
45 - 64	5,336	9,530	29.8	27.0	2,707	91,100	46.1	1,458.1	27.3	129,666	19.7	66
65 - 74	1,194	7,706	13.7	41.0	1,040	49,400	72.0	504.9	42.3	37,284	7.5	55
75+	1,173	4,997	8.2	46.0	585	85,000	88.0	575.3	49.0	20,880	4.2	51
Women												
0 - 4	1,604	10,000	78.1	3.0	802	10,300	8.8	48.7	3.0	48,492	61.2	78
5 - 14	2,978	9,905	73.8	7.0	1,800	30,100	9.1	209.1	7.0	92,125	56.9	77
15 - 44	11,010	9,889	63.9	12.0	5,233	231,800	12.8	1,323.1	12.0	258,945	47.7	75
45 - 64	5,458	9,701	34.8	26.0	2,800	70,000	44.5	1,432.0	26.2	137,619	21.9	63
65 - 74	2,489	8,581	17.6	40.0	1,289	61,500	74.7	1,016.9	40.9	45,976	8.7	50
75+	2,283	6,786	10.8	56.0	1,087	285,200	92.5	1,382.6	60.6	28,905	4.3	39

Table 6.1: continued

	Pop. (thou)	I(0)	Life expect	GHS LLI rate	GHS n	Comm pop	Comm LLI	All LLI (thou)	d(x)	LWD(x)	HLE(x)	Ratio
1991												
Men												
0 - 4	1,761	10,000	73.2	4.0	891	12,100	9.1	71.1	4.0	47,258	59.9	82
5 - 14	3,231	9,895	69.0	7.0	1,830	46,300	9.1	227.1	7.0	92,228	55.7	81
15 - 44	11,314	9,874	59.1	10.0	4,808	350,000	14.4	1,146.8	10.1	262,735	46.5	79
45 - 64	5,433	9,547	30.5	25.0	2,628	91,100	46.1	1,377.5	25.4	133,694	20.6	67
65 - 74	2,027	7,893	14.2	40.0	967	49,400	72.0	826.6	40.8	39,902	7.9	56
75+	1,229	5,259	8.5	46.0	606	85,000	88.0	601.0	48.9	22,840	4.3	51
Women												
0 - 4	1,670	10,000	78.7	3.0	891	10,300	8.8	50.7	3.0	48,500	63.0	80
5 - 14	3,050	9,919	74.3	5.0	1,768	30,100	9.1	153.7	5.0	94,166	58.7	79
15 - 44	10,987	9,904	64.4	11.0	4,959	231,800	12.8	1,212.7	11.0	262,818	49.2	76
45 - 64	5,527	9,727	35.2	25.0	2,789	70,000	44.5	1,395.4	25.2	139,775	23.1	66
65 - 74	2,479	8,682	17.9	34.0	1,212	61,500	74.7	867.9	35.0	51,551	9.8	55
75+	2,391	6,917	11.0	51.0	983	285,200	92.5	1,337.8	56.0	33,516	4.8	44
1992												
Men												
0 - 4	1,772	10,000	73.7	5.0	870	12,200	9.1	89.1	5.0	47,140	59.7	81
5 - 14	3,282	9,913	69.4	8.0	1,780	48,810	9.1	263.1	8.0	91,129	55.5	80
15 - 44	11,192	9,894	59.5	10.0	4,610	357,500	14.4	1,134.9	10.1	263,184	46.4	78
45 - 64	5,571	9,570	30.9	26.0	2,739	86,100	46.1	1,465.8	26.3	132,388	20.4	66
65 - 74	2,049	8,016	14.5	40.0	1,039	49,700	72.0	835.5	40.8	39,978	7.9	54
75+	1,234	5,497	8.9	49.0	601	98,200	88.0	643.0	52.1	23,301	4.2	48
Women												
0 - 4	1,683	10,000	79.2	2.0	840	10,200	8.8	34.4	2.0	48,670	61.9	78
5 - 14	3,104	9,932	74.8	7.0	1,694	31,100	9.1	217.9	7.0	92,207	57.4	77
15 - 44	10,855	9,919	64.9	13.0	4,938	242,200	12.8	1,410.7	13.0	257,296	48.2	74
45 - 64	5,658	9,740	35.7	26.0	2,864	64,800	44.5	1,483.1	26.2	138,147	22.7	64
65 - 74	2,488	8,756	18.3	38.0	1,241	60,800	74.7	967.8	38.9	48,337	9.5	52
75+	2,391	7,059	11.5	52.0	972	327,600	92.5	1,376.0	57.5	34,551	4.9	42

Table 6.2: Persons present in communal establishments, total and those with limiting long-term illness, by age and sex, from 1991 Census

	Males		Females	
	Total	With LLI	Total	With LLI
0 - 4	12,218	1,116	10,190	894
5 - 14	48,161	4,383	30,878	2,810
15 - 29	256,895	24,215	184,906	15,564
30 - 44	98,755	26,921	54,695	15,168
45 - 54	46,325	17,876	31,098	11,286
55 - 59	19,096	9,118	15,141	6,642
60 - 64	21,939	13,213	19,847	11,507
65 - 74	49,643	35,745	60,972	45,537
75 - 84	60,753	52,258	149,292	134,889
85+	34,119	31,224	167,741	158,410

Source: Total from 1991 Census Great Britain report, Table 11. Numbers with LLI estimated from 1991 Census Great Britain report, Table 13. These figures are used for estimating the communal establishment LLI rates shown in Table 6.1.

6.2 Calculation of trends in health expectancy using measures of disability for people aged 65 and over, General Household Survey 1976-1991

This section concerns trends in health expectancy based on more severe aspects of disability for people aged 65 and over living in England and Wales. Three measures of disability have been included: the ability to walk up and down stairs without help, the ability to go outdoors without help, and independence in performing activities of daily living (ADLs). ADLs are activities which people perform habitually and universally, such as bathing, dressing, transfer, feeding, getting to the toilet and continence.

Methodology

To examine trends over time, it is necessary to have comparable data. As mentioned in chapter 5, comparability of data is affected by question wording, reference population and other aspects of data collection and production. All these aspects were closely investigated prior to analysis but some differences between the surveys did not become apparent until results had been produced which seemed incorrect or contained many missing cases.

Only a limited number of aspects of disability have been monitored over time using exactly the same questions. The Elderly at Home Survey (1976) and the 1980 and 1985 GHS Elderly Sections used very similar question wording, whereas the 1991 GHS Elderly Section changed the selection of items and question wording to be more comparable with the Disability Surveys (OPCS, 1985-1986).

A number of aspects of disability were selected which were similarly defined in the Elderly at Home Survey of 1976 and the GHS Elderly Sections of 1980 and 1985: four activities of daily living (bathing, transfer from bed, feeding, getting to the toilet), the ability to walk up and down stairs without help and the ability to go outdoors without help. Although the question wording was different, the same aspects of disability were selected from the 1991 GHS Elderly Section in order to examine trends in health expectancy between 1976 and 1991. It was assumed that the change in question wording would not affect the comparability of the results (see Appendix A).

The four activities of daily living were used to construct a scale similar to the Katz ADL scale (Katz, 1963; Katz and Akpom, 1976). Katz developed an index of overall function using a Guttman-type approach to analyse the performance of basic functions of patients with chronic conditions. The result was the following index which parallels the order of development of primary functions in children and the order of recovery of primary functions in disabled patients:

A   Independent in feeding, continence, transferring, going to the toilet, dressing, and bathing.

B   Independent in all but one of these functions.

C   Independent in all but bathing and one additional function.

D   Independent in all but bathing, dressing, and one additional function.

E   Independent in all but bathing, dressing, going to the toilet, and one additional function.

F   Independent in all but bathing, dressing, going to the toilet, transferring, and one additional function.

G   Dependent in all six functions.

Other Dependent in at least 2 functions, but not classifiable as C, D, E, or F.

The ADLs dressing and continence were not included in all the General Household Surveys and were therefore dropped from the index. In support of the hypothesis that the index parallels the order of development of primary functions, the four surveys included very few cases which fell in the "Other" category. These cases were excluded from the analysis.

For the purposes of the analysis, the index was collapsed into two categories:

1   Independent in all ADLs (i.e. the ability to bath oneself, get in and out of bed, feed oneself and get to the toilet without the help of another person);

2   Dependent in one or more ADLs

Table 6.4 shows the proportion of elderly who could not manage to perform all four ADLs independently. Life expectancies with the ability to perform the four ADLs independently were calculated for 1976, 1980, 1985 and 1991.

In addition, health expectancy figures were derived from measures of the ability to get up and down stairs without help and the ability to get out of doors without help. The proportions of elderly who could not perform these tasks unaided, are shown in Tables 6.5 and 6.6.

Figures throughout are for England and Wales, except for the Elderly at Home Survey (1976) which only covered England. It was assumed that in 1976 the prevalence rates of physical disability for England applied equally to England and Wales.

The surveys included in the analysis covered private households only. The private household data was adjusted to account for disabled people in communal establishments based on the rate of disablement among elderly people in communal establishments compared with those from private households from the UK Disability Surveys of 1985-6. This approach makes a fairly crude assumption about the relationship between levels of disability in communal establishments and levels in private households, acceptable in

Table 6.3: Predicted total life expectancy in long-term ill-health, from GHS

	Male years	Female years
1976	11.7	14.1
1981	12.4	16.1
1985	13.1	15.8
1988	13.9	16.9
1991	13.3	15.7

Source: Table 6.1

Table 6.4: Proportion of those aged 65 and over who were not able to perform ADLs independently by age and sex, 1976-1991

Age	1976*	1980**	1985**	1991**
Men	%	%	%	%
65-69	4	4	4	2
70-74	8	6	4	3
75-79	18	8	11	5
80-84	25	18	15	9
85 and over	43	31	23	20
Women				
65-69	6	4	3	3
70-74	15	8	6	3
75-79	22	10	9	6
80-84	36	13	19	7
85 and over	54	36	33	21
Bases:				
Men				
65-69	327	751	472	544
70-74	238	545	410	412
75-79	262	321	297	334
80-84	113	168	137	202
85 and over	54	55	44	66
Women				
65-69	398	906	549	686
70-74	391	714	573	520
75-79	426	566	460	477
80-84	262	280	281	144
85 and over	151	202	144	160

Table 6.5: Proportion of those aged 65 and over who were not able to get up and down stairs without help by age and sex, 1976-1991

Age	1976*	1980**	1985**	1991**
Men	%	%	%	%
65-69	4	4	4	2
70-74	8	6	4	3
75-79	18	8	11	5
80-84	25	18	15	9
85 and over	43	31	23	20
Women				
65-69	6	4	3	3
70-74	15	8	6	3
75-79	22	10	9	6
80-84	36	13	19	7
85 and over	54	36	33	21
Bases:				
Men				
65-69	327	751	472	544
70-74	238	545	410	412
75-79	262	321	297	334
80-84	113	168	137	202
85 and over	54	55	44	66
Women				
65-69	398	906	549	686
70-74	391	714	573	520
75-79	426	566	460	477
80-84	262	280	281	144
85 and over	151	202	144	160

* Source: Elderly at Home (England only)
** Sources: General Household Survey 1980, 1985, 1991 (England and Wales)

Table 6.6: **Proportion of those aged 65 and over who were not able to get out of doors without help by age and sex, 1976-1991**

Age	1976[*]	1980[**]	1985[**]	1991[**]
Men	%	%	%	%
65-69	3	3	5	4
70-74	5	8	6	3
75-79	11	8	11	6
80-84	15	17	15	13
85 and over	33	38	23	37
Women				
65-69	6	6	8	6
70-74	13	10	11	8
75-79	19	16	18	14
80-84	26	34	33	21
85 and over	56	52	60	50
Bases:				
Men				
65-69	*327*	*740*	*456*	*553*
70-74	*238*	*538*	*403*	*417*
75-79	*262*	*318*	*290*	*336*
80-84	*113*	*167*	*137*	*204*
85 and over	*54*	*56*	*44*	*67*
Women				
65-69	*398*	*894*	*536*	*691*
70-74	*391*	*701*	*560*	*522*
75-79	*426*	*560*	*457*	*478*
80-84	*262*	*277*	*279*	*349*
85 and over	*151*	*197*	*146*	*161*

[*] Source: Elderly at Home (England only)
[**] Sources: General Household Survey 1980, 1985, and 1991
(England and Wales)

this case, as noted earlier, because the vast majority of disabled people are in private households[3].

Health expectancies were calculated by Sullivan's method, applying age-specific physical disability rates to life table estimates. Life table estimates for 1976, 1980, 1985 and 1991 were provided by the Government Actuary's Department.

Results

Table 6.7 shows that life expectancy with the ability to perform ADLs independently has increased in this period for both elderly men and women; for example, disability free life expectancy of men aged 65 has increased from 11.0 years in 1976 to 13.6 years in 1991. (The consistent trend over time suggests that this improvement is not overly sensitive to changes in question wording.)

The ability to get up and down stairs without help and the ability to get out of doors without help show a different pattern. Tables 6.8 and 6.9 give the overall impression of a period of equilibrium; health expectancy derived from these

measures of mobility has increased in identical proportions to total life expectancy, with the result that the proportion of remaining years of life free of these disabilities has almost stabilised in this period. It must be noted that the figures for mobility are not very consistent in the highest age groups, in particular the difference between the 1976 results and the results in following years is sufficient to throw doubt on the comparability of the data from the Elderly at Home Survey with the subsequent GHS data. These apparent differences over time may be real or may be caused by differences in the collection and coding of the data or be due to small sample sizes in the oldest age groups.

Although women had longer life expectancies than men, a larger proportion of this time was spent with physical disabilities. This was true for all three measures of physical disability. The greatest sex differences appeared with the ability to go outdoors without help (see also chapter 10). However, the results indicate that sex differences may be declining for the ability to perform ADLs independently.

6.3 Discussion

Figure 6.3 shows the trend in life expectancy, and health expectancy measured both by limiting long-standing illness and by the three measures of disability, for men and women aged 65. The results are variable. Those based on the Katz ADL scale are encouraging. For men, the proportion of remaining years of life with the ability to perform ADLs independently has increased from 88% to 95%, suggesting compression of morbidity in relation to the ability to perform these activities.

By contrast, the trends relating to limiting long-standing illness and mobility are less favourable. For men aged 65, the proportion of remaining years free of limiting long-standing illness remained fairly stationary at about 55%, for mobility outdoors at 91% and for climbing stairs at 94%.

---

[3]Based on the Disability Surveys, which included comparable measures of disability in private households and communal establishments. Using a mobility measure (the ability to walk 50 yards or more), the following estimator of proportion p_C, of people in communal establishments who were disabled at the time of General Household surveys, was constructed:

$$\hat{p}_C = \frac{p_H p_{D,C}(1-p_{D,H})}{p_H(p_{D,C}-p_{D,H}) + p_{D,C}(1-p_{D,H})}$$

where p_H is the proportion of people in private households who were disabled in the corresponding GHS;
p_{DH} is the proportion in private households in the Disability Survey with mobility problems;
p_{DC} is the proportion in communal establishments in the Disability Survey with mobility problems;

This formula was applied separately to each age and sex group, using GHS data in 1976, 1980, 1985 and 1991. To convert this to an estimate of numbers of disabled people in private households and communal establishments combined, it was in addition necessary to estimate the proportion of people in each age/sex group living in the two types of accommodation. This was done by the same interpolation method as is described in section 7.1.

Figure 6.3: Trends in Healthy Life Expectancy at age 65, 1976 - 1991

Men

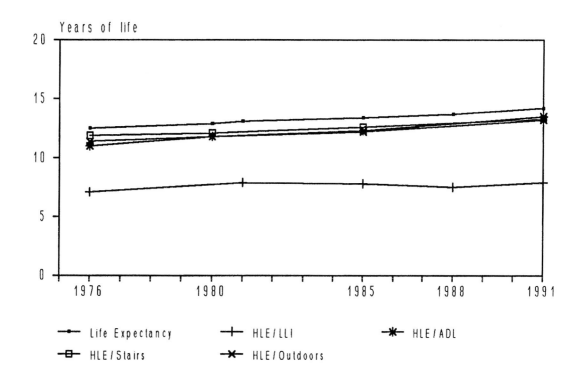

Women

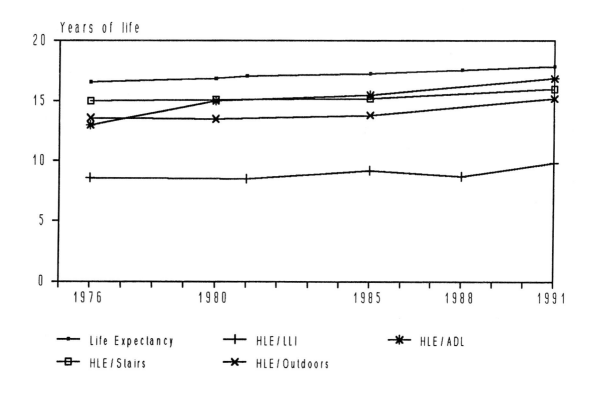

Table 6.7: Life expectancies with the ability to perform ADLs (bathing, transfer from bed, feeding and getting to the toilet) independently by age and sex, 1976-1991

	1976			1980			1985			1991		
	TLE[1]	DFLE[2]	DFLE/TLE[3]	TLE[1]	DFLE[2]	DFLE/TLE[3]	TLE[1]	DFLE[2]	DFLE/TLE[3]	TLE[1]	DFLE[2]	DFLE/TLE[3]
Age	years	years	%	years	years	%	years	years	%	years	years	%
Men												
65-69	12.5	11.0	88	12.9	11.8	91	13.4	12.3	92	14.3	13.6	95
70-74	9.7	8.0	83	10.0	8.9	89	10.5	9.5	90	11.2	10.4	93
75-79	7.4	5.6	76	7.6	6.5	85	8.0	6.9	86	8.6	7.8	91
80-84	5.6	3.9	69	5.7	4.4	77	6.0	5.0	83	6.5	5.6	87
85 and over	4.1	2.4	58	4.3	3.0	69	4.5	3.5	77	4.8	3.8	80
Women												
65-69	16.5	13.0	79	16.9	15.0	89	17.4	15.5	89	18.1	16.9	93
70-74	12.9	9.4	73	13.3	11.4	86	13.8	11.8	86	14.5	13.3	92
75-79	9.8	6.5	67	10.1	8.3	83	10.6	8.6	82	11.2	10.0	90
80-84	7.1	4.1	58	7.4	5.7	77	7.8	5.9	75	8.4	7.3	87
85 and over	5.1	2.6	51	5.3	3.6	67	5.6	3.9	70	6.1	4.9	81

[1] Total life expectancy
[2] Disability-free life expectancy
[3] Proportion of remaining life free of disability (the proportions were calculated with DFLE measured to 2 decimal places and may differ by 1% when calculating the proportions from the values given in the table)

Table 6.8: Life expectancies with the ability to manage stairs and steps without help by age and sex, 1976-1991

	1976			1980			1985			1991		
	TLE[1]	DFLE[2]	DFLE/TLE[3]	TLE[1]	DFLE[2]	DFLE/TLE[3]	TLE[1]	DFLE[2]	DFLE/TLE[3]	TLE[1]	DFLE[2]	DFLE/TLE[3]
Age	years	years	%	years	years	%	years	years	%	years	years	%
Men												
65-69	12.5	11.9	96	12.9	12.1	94	13.4	12.6	94	14.3	13.3	93
70-74	9.7	9.1	94	10.0	9.2	92	10.5	9.7	92	11.2	10.3	92
75-79	7.4	6.8	92	7.6	6.8	89	8.0	7.1	89	8.6	7.6	89
80-84	5.6	5.1	92	5.7	4.7	82	6.0	5.1	85	6.5	5.5	84
85 and over	4.1	3.6	89	4.3	3.0	71	4.5	3.4	75	4.8	3.6	76
Women												
65-69	16.5	15.0	91	16.9	15.1	89	17.4	15.2	87	18.1	16.0	89
70-74	12.9	11.4	88	13.3	11.5	86	13.8	11.6	84	14.5	12.4	86
75-79	9.8	8.3	85	10.1	8.3	82	10.6	8.4	79	11.2	9.1	82
80-84	7.1	5.8	82	7.4	5.7	77	7.8	5.8	75	8.4	6.4	77
85 and over	5.1	4.0	79	5.3	3.8	71	5.6	4.0	72	6.1	4.3	71

[1] Total life expectancy
[2] Disability-free life expectancy
[3] Proportion of remaining life free of disability (the proportions were calculated with DFLE measured to 2 decimal places and may differ by 1% when calculating the proportions from the values given in the table)

Table 6.9: Life expectancies with the ability to get out of doors without help by age and sex, 1976-1991

Age	1976			1980			1985			1991		
	TLE[1]	DFLE[2]	DFLE/TLE[3]	TLE[1]	DFLE[2]	DFLE/TLE[3]	TLE[1]	DFLE[2]	DFLE/TLE[3]	TLE[1]	DFLE[2]	DFLE/TLE[3]
	years	years	%	years	years	%	years	years	%	years	years	%
Men												
65-69	12.5	11.4	91	12.9	11.8	91	13.4	12.2	91	14.3	13.2	92
70-74	9.7	8.5	88	10.0	8.9	89	10.5	9.3	89	11.2	10.1	90
75-79	7.4	6.3	85	7.6	6.5	85	8.0	6.8	85	8.6	7.4	86
80-84	5.6	4.3	76	5.7	4.7	82	6.0	4.9	82	6.5	5.0	78
85 and over	4.1	2.6	63	4.3	3.3	77	4.5	3.5	77	4.8	3.1	64
Women												
65-69	16.5	13.6	82	16.9	13.5	80	17.4	13.8	79	18.1	15.2	84
70-74	12.9	10.0	78	13.3	10.0	75	13.8	10.3	75	14.5	11.6	80
75-79	9.8	7.0	71	10.1	6.8	68	10.6	7.1	67	11.2	8.3	74
80-84	7.1	4.3	61	7.4	4.2	57	7.8	4.4	57	8.4	5.6	67
85 and over	5.1	2.7	53	5.3	2.5	47	5.6	2.6	47	6.1	3.4	56

[1] Total life expectancy
[2] Disability-free life expectancy
[3] Proportion of remaining life free of disability (the proportions were calculated with DFLE measured to 2 decimal places and may differ by 1% when calculating the proportions from the values given in the table)

The same pattern is broadly true for women though the proportion of healthy life is generally less. One exception is in relation to outdoors mobility where there was a sudden improvement between 1985 and 1991 (see Table 6.9). However, the mobility question in 1991 was significantly different in format from earlier years (see Appendix A), and this one result may not be too significant[4].

There is a some similarity between these patterns and those reported by Crimmins et al (1989) for the US. Between 1970 and 1980 for people aged 65 there was no improvement in the proportion of self-reported disability-free life, but a marked improvement in relation to confinement to bed, which is closely related to one of the measures in our ADL scale.

What does this pattern signify? One argument is that the lack of improvement in self rated health is due to greater awareness of ill-health combined perhaps with improving diagnostic techniques identifying diseases earlier and with greater sophistication so that, for instance, general aches are now labelled as arthritis. Mobility, especially outdoors, may have been reduced by social as well as health changes: for example, the rise in private and decline in public transport, and increased fears of vulnerability among the elderly. On the other hand the ability to perform specific tasks might seem to some a much more reliable measure of disability. (But here too changes other than those in health can be important, such as improvements in rehabilitation and aids for managing disability.)

An alternative explanation, which echoes Manton's theory of equilibrium (see chapter 1) is that what we see is the consequence of a differential response of the health care system. ADLs are at the high end of disability; particularly the ones in our scale. In the 1991 GHS, only 6% of all people over 65 were not able to perform these. By contrast limiting long-standing illness is reported by 43% of all people over 65. The consequence of a health care system which was increasingly targeted on the most disabled but away from the less disabled would be to produce the observed trend.

The implications of these findings, if projected forwards, would seem to be that future gains in life expectancy among the elderly people may well be accompanied by a rise in the amount of chronic disability, particularly at lower levels of disability and/or self-perceived health status. However the signs of improvement in LLI for all people in 1991 and possibly 1992 may be significant.

These conclusions are of course subject to the caveats raised in chapters 4 and 5. In particular Sullivan's method, which has been used here, provides a picture of trends in disability that tends to lag some years behind current changes in disablement rates. Consequently any evolving compression or expansion of morbidity may not be evident until some time after it has begun.

[4]However, this does not explain why a similar improvement was not found for men. When results become available from the 1994 GHS Elderly Section, which reverted to the 1985 questions, it will be possible to determine whether this improvement was a real change in healthy life expectancy.

7   Inequalities in healthy life expectancy from the 1991 Census

Inequalities in health between social groups in England and Wales raise issues of social justice. Indeed, the first target of the WHO (Europe region) "Health for all by the year 2000" strategy was to bring about a reduction in differences in health status between groups and countries, by improving the level of health in disadvantaged groups.

This chapter examines

- Health expectancy (HE) from the limiting long-standing illness (LLI) question in the 1991 Census, comparing this figure with estimates derived from other sources (section 7.2).

- Geographical variations in health expectancy based on the limiting long-standing illness question from the 1991 census, which by comparison with previous sources is able to provide a far more detailed breakdown (section 7.3).

- Explanations of variations between geographical areas in health expectancy (section 7.4).

- Variations between ethnic groups in health expectancy (section 7.5).

7.1 Methodology

The 1991 Census determined people with limiting long-standing illness (LLI) by asking the question described in section 5.3. Census tabulations and small area statistics provide the source of information for LLI in this sections. Tabulations relating to this question are given in the special Census volume *Limiting Long-term Illness*.

Figures throughout are for England & Wales (unless otherwise stated). Population is OPCS final mid-year estimate for 1991 (produced September 1993), which are used for calculating mortality rates, though Census populations are generally used for the calculation of LLI rates. Where rates are shown as age-standardised, the standardisation has been undertaken based on England & Wales population totals in the following age groups: 0-4, 5-14, 15-24, ..., 75-84, 85+. Mortality figures relate to the average of the years 1990-2 combined, including foreigners but excluding people who die abroad. These figures were supplied by Health Statistics of OPCS from death registrations.

Life table estimates are prepared directly from these sources, by the conventional method for abridged tables. Health expectancies are calculated by Sullivan's method, applying age-specific LLI rates to the life table estimates of $_nL_x$, the estimated number of life years lived between x and x+n of a hypothetical birth cohort experiencing life table mortality rates. This method was described in chapter 4.

7.2 Healthy life expectancy

Nationally 6.5m answered 'yes' to the question on whether they had a limiting long-standing illness. Of these 6.0m were in private households and 0.5m in communal establishments. Table 7.1 shows the life expectancy and health expectancy in 1991 at various ages. On average about 85 per cent of life years are lived in good health. There is a sharp tail-off in HE in older age groups, so that by 75 less than half of remaining life is likely to be in good health. This age gradient is broadly similar to that found in the 1985-8 Disability Surveys: this was discussed further in section 5.3 and Figure 5.4.

Table 7.1 shows that women have longer life expectancies, and also longer healthy life expectancy, but that men enjoy a greater proportion of life in good health. This is true at all ages, and is in line with previous findings.

7.3 Area variations

The scale of the Census permits the calculation of HE in much greater detail than has hitherto been possible. Tables 7.2 and 7.3 show life expectancies and health expectancies using the Standard regions and Regional Health Authority areas of England and Wales. For life expectancies at birth, there are regional variations of 3 years for men, 2½ for women. For health expectancy at birth the variations are considerably greater: 6½ years for men, 5 years for women. These variations differentiate the north and west of England and Wales from the south and east.

A striking feature of these tables is the correlation between age-standardised disability rates (shown in the first column) and life expectancy. People in the south and east not only live longer, but enjoy better health rates. The consequence is that regional variations in HE at birth are much greater, 6 years for men, 5 years for women. The national pattern is similar, though it is noteworthy that while the North-West has the lowest life expectancies, HE is lowest in Wales. To summarise, a man in south-east England can expect to live 89 per cent of his 74½ years in good health, while in contrast a man in Wales would expect to live 82 per cent of his 73 years in good health.

Comparison between figures at birth and age 65 show that all these trends persist through life. For example, a man at age 65 in the South East can expect to live 53 per cent of his remaining 9.0 years in good health while a man in Wales would expect 47 per cent of his remaining 8.7 years in good health.

The pattern of regional variations shown in Table 7.2 corresponds very closely indeed to previous estimates of disability-free life expectancy prepared from the 1985-8

Table 7.1: Abridged life table and healthy life expectancy based on 1991 Census LLI, England and Wales

	Men				Women			
Age	l_x	e_x	d_x	$hale_x$	l_x	e_x	d_x	$hale_x$
0- 4	100,000	73.43	21	63.68	100,000	79.00	17	67.41
5-14	99,032	69.12	27	59.38	99,242	74.58	22	62.99
15-29	98,836	59.25	35	49.76	99,103	64.68	33	53.28
30-44	97,665	44.87	60	35.79	98,631	49.95	56	39.00
45-54	95,586	30.68	120	22.32	97,358	35.51	118	25.26
55-64	91,391	21.86	261	14.34	94,632	26.39	212	17.04
65-74	79,582	14.36	348	8.54	87,202	18.21	318	10.27
75-84	54,243	8.74	454	4.48	70,183	11.41	493	5.11
85 and over	20,243	5.01	608	1.96	38,954	6.56	675	2.13

d_x denotes the Limiting Longstanding Illness rate per 1,000

Table 7.2: Life expectancy and healthy life expectancy, at birth and at age 65, standard regions of England and Wales

	Disability rate[1] per 1000	Expectation at birth		Expectation at 65	
		Life	HLE	Life	HLE
Men					
North	141	72.3	61.2	13.6	7.5
Yorks & Humberside	131	72.7	62.2	13.9	7.8
East Midlands	119	73.5	63.7	14.3	8.5
East Anglia	99	75.0	66.2	15.1	9.5
South East	95	74.7	66.4	15.0	9.5
Greater London	111	73.1	63.9	14.5	8.9
South West	104	74.6	65.6	15.1	9.5
West Midlands	120	73.0	63.3	14.0	8.2
North West	139	72.1	61.2	13.6	7.6
Wales	158	73.1	60.4	14.1	7.4
Women					
North	152	77.8	65.5	17.3	9.3
Yorks & Humberside	148	78.3	66.0	17.8	9.4
East Midlands	136	78.9	67.4	18.1	10.1
East Anglia	120	80.1	69.5	18.8	11.2
South East	117	79.9	69.6	18.7	11.2
Greater London	134	79.3	67.7	18.6	10.7
South West	121	80.2	69.4	19.0	11.3
West Midlands	140	78.5	66.8	18.0	9.9
North West	155	77.7	65.2	17.3	9.3
Wales	166	78.9	64.9	18.1	9.4

[1] Standardised by age

OPCS Disability Surveys (Bebbington, 1993, Table 6), despite the fact that the two approaches display different overall health expectancies. This confirms the robustness of these findings to quite different approaches to measuring health. Regional variations in health at birth measured from the Census are however rather larger than those obtained from the Disability Surveys (5 years for men, 3 years for women).

These results are highly significant to issues of equity as they relate to central government resource allocation, which for health regions in particular was determined until 1995 largely by death rates. The results of Table 7.3 suggest that the correlation between mortality and long term illness rates vindicates the use of mortality data as a surrogate for morbidity data in making resource allocations to regions. However, it also indicates that were the funding in England to be based on a criterion of equity in health expectancy rather than in mortality, much the same pattern of allocation would obtain but that *differentials* between regions would be considerably higher. This concurs with findings by Carr-Hill et al (1990).

Table 7.3: Life expectancy and healthy life expectancy, at birth and at age 65, regional health authorities of England and Wales

	Disability rate[1] per 1000	Expectation at birth		Expectation at birth	
		Life	HLE	Life	HLE
Men					
Northern	154	72.1	60.4	13.4	7.1
Yorkshire	127	73.0	63.0	14.1	8.0
Trent	132	73.4	62.8	14.2	8.1
East Anglian	103	75.1	66.2	15.2	9.5
North West Thames	101	74.2	65.7	14.9	9.4
North East Thames	117	73.4	64.0	14.4	8.7
South East Thames	112	73.7	64.5	14.7	9.1
South West Thames	94	75.0	66.9	15.2	9.8
Wessex	104	74.8	66.1	15.1	9.6
Oxford	95	74.7	66.6	14.8	9.4
South Western	111	74.6	65.2	15.1	9.3
West Midlands	124	73.1	63.2	14.0	8.2
Mersey	143	72.5	61.5	13.7	7.8
North Western	144	72.0	61.0	13.5	7.5
Wales	162	73.2	60.4	14.1	7.4
Women					
Northern	160	77.6	64.7	17.2	8.9
Yorkshire	142	78.7	66.8	18.0	9.7
Trent	147	78.9	66.5	18.1	9.6
East Anglian	122	80.2	69.4	18.9	1.1
North West Thames	124	80.0	69.0	18.9	1.0
North East Thames	137	79.4	67.5	18.5	0.3
South East Thames	129	79.6	68.4	18.8	0.8
South West Thames	115	80.3	70.0	19.0	1.4
Wessex	120	80.3	69.5	19.0	1.2
Oxford	117	79.8	69.5	18.7	0.9
South Western	125	80.2	69.1	19.0	1.0
West Midlands	143	78.7	66.7	18.1	9.8
Mersey	154	78.2	65.6	17.6	9.4
North Western	160	77.7	64.9	17.4	9.0
Wales	169	79.0	64.8	18.2	9.3

[1] Standardised by age.

Table 7.4 (see pages 38-41) shows, similarly, life expectancies and HE for each major local authority area in England and Wales. The size of variation in HE between areas at this level is perhaps surprising. It reaches nearly 12 years for men, 10 years for women, between Surrey and the south-west boroughs of Outer London at best, to Glamorgan and areas around Manchester at worst. This amounts to an expectation, for men, of a 20 per cent longer life span in good health in the former areas compared with the latter.

Figure 7.1 summarises these findings by showing the positions of each local authority in terms of the average life expectancy and the expected number of years in ill-health. This figure confirms the very strong relationship between short life expectancy and amount of ill-health. Local authorities above the regression line are those in which morbidity is high in relation to mortality, and those below have low morbidity in relation to mortality.

7.4 Causes of area variations

We are here concerned with social rather than medical or environmental explanations of geographical variations in overall health (for which see Britton, 1989; Britton et al, 1989). A number of explanations have been proposed, and it is of interest to investigate to what extent they can describe the variations in HLE between the administrative areas shown in Table 7.4.

Social class

Social class differences in health have been well established since the Black Report (1980). What has been less clear is whether low social class is the cause of poorer health expectancy or the consequence of ill-health; but available evidence does suggest that it is at least in part the cause (Fox et al, 1985; Bebbington, 1993). Social class is here measured from Table 90 of the 1991 small area statistics (SAS) as:

$$\frac{\text{Number of people living in h'holds in social class IV or V}}{\text{Number of people living in economically active h'holds}} \times 100$$

Household social class is defined by head of household.

Moser et al (1987) have drawn attention to the strong relationship between unemployment and high mortality rates observed in the OPCS Longitudinal Survey. For this reason we also examine the unemployment rate as a predictor of healthy life expectancy, measured as the percentage of all economically active adults who are unemployed (SAS, Table 8).

Figure 7.1: Life expectancy at birth and expected years of ill-health, local authorities in England and Wales, 1991

Men

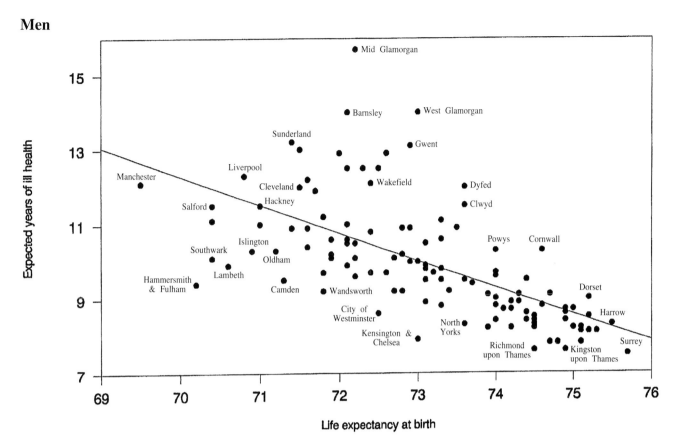

Women

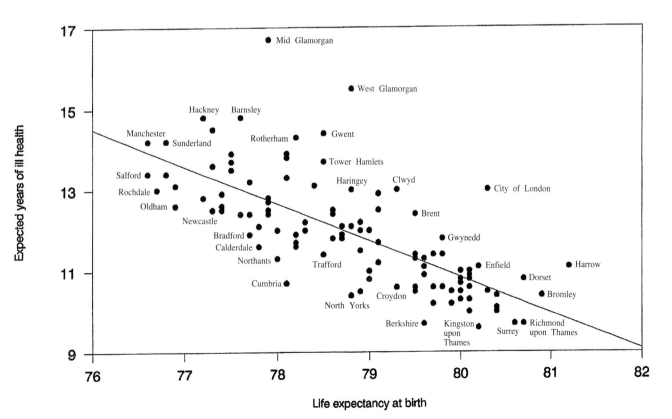

Table 7.4: **Life expectancy and healthy life expectancy, at birth and at age 65, by sex and local authority areas of England and Wales**

	Disability rate[1] per 1000	Expectation at birth		Expectation at 65	
		Life	HLE	Life	HLE
Men					
City of London	86	73.4	64.2	n.a.	n.a.
Barking & Dagenham	129	72.2	62.1	13.8	8.1
Barnet	91	75.2	67.1	15.5	9.9
Bexley	98	74.9	66.3	14.8	9.3
Brent	114	73.1	63.6	15.1	9.2
Bromley	92	75.1	67.0	15.0	9.6
Camden	121	71.3	61.8	14.5	8.7
Croydon	99	74.0	65.6	14.6	9.3
Ealing	114	72.7	63.5	14.3	8.9
Enfield	101	74.2	65.5	14.8	9.3
Greenwich	123	72.4	62.7	13.7	8.1
Hackney	152	71.0	59.5	13.4	7.3
Hammersmith & Fulham	126	70.2	60.8	13.8	8.0
Haringey	123	73.0	63.0	14.2	8.3
Harrow	92	75.5	67.2	15.5	9.9
Havering	99	74.4	66.0	14.7	9.2
Hillingdon	95	74.2	66.0	14.8	9.4
Hounslow	105	73.3	64.5	14.8	9.3
Islington	137	70.9	60.6	14.0	8.1
Kensington & Chelsea	95	73.0	65.1	15.1	9.9
Kingston upon Thames	86	74.9	67.3	15.1	10.1
Lambeth	132	70.6	60.7	13.8	8.1
Lewisham	125	72.1	62.2	13.9	8.0
Merton	97	74.5	66.0	15.1	9.5
Newham	143	71.4	60.5	13.4	7.4
Redbridge	107	73.9	64.8	14.7	8.9
Richmond upon Thames	86	74.5	66.9	15.1	9.8
Southwark	136	70.4	60.3	13.6	7.9
Sutton	93	75.0	66.8	15.1	9.6
Tower Hamlets	150	70.4	59.3	13.4	7.6
Waltham Forest	118	73.2	63.5	14.3	8.5
Wandsworth	118	71.8	62.6	13.8	8.1
City of Westminster	104	72.5	63.9	15.4	9.9
Bolton	144	71.8	60.6	13.6	7.3
Bury	128	72.8	62.6	13.7	7.7
Manchester	168	69.5	57.4	12.9	6.8
Oldham	136	71.2	60.9	13.3	7.5
Rochdale	143	71.6	60.7	13.3	7.3
Salford	157	70.4	58.9	12.8	6.7
Stockport	110	73.1	64.2	13.9	8.4
Tameside	137	71.9	61.3	13.3	7.3
Trafford	114	73.6	64.1	14.5	8.7
Wigan	160	72.1	59.6	13.1	6.7
Knowsley	171	71.5	58.5	13.0	6.8
Liverpool	166	70.8	58.5	13.0	7.0
St Helens	160	72.3	59.8	13.4	6.7
Sefton	135	72.8	61.9	14.2	8.3
Wirral	137	72.1	61.5	13.6	7.8
Barnsley	180	72.1	58.1	13.3	6.2
Doncaster	162	72.6	59.7	13.8	7.0
Rotherham	159	72.5	60.0	13.5	6.7
Sheffield	137	72.9	62.0	13.8	7.5
Gateshead	160	71.6	59.4	12.9	6.6
Newcastle upon Tyne	146	71.0	60.0	13.2	7.3
North Tyneside	141	72.1	61.1	13.2	7.3
South Tyneside	157	71.7	59.8	13.1	6.9
Sunderland	175	71.4	58.2	12.9	6.1
Birmingham	131	71.9	61.7	13.7	8.0

Table 7.4: continued

	Disability rate[1] per 1000	Expectation at birth		Expectation at 65	
		Life	HLE	Life	HLE
Men					
Coventry	121	72.2	62.6	13.8	8.3
Dudley	117	73.3	63.8	13.9	8.1
Sandwell	136	71.6	61.2	13.3	7.4
Solihull	100	75.0	66.3	15.0	9.4
Walsall	135	72.2	61.7	13.5	7.5
Wolverhampton	134	72.1	61.6	13.8	7.9
Bradford	129	71.9	61.8	13.7	7.8
Calderdale	125	71.8	62.1	13.7	7.9
Kirklees	122	72.6	62.9	13.7	7.9
Leeds	123	72.9	62.9	14.3	8.2
Wakefield	153	72.4	60.3	13.4	6.7
Avon	103	74.3	65.4	14.9	9.3
Bedfordshire	98	73.9	65.7	14.5	9.0
Berkshire	88	74.8	67.0	14.9	9.7
Buckinghamshire	89	74.7	66.9	14.8	9.4
Cambridgeshire	96	74.9	66.5	15.0	9.5
Cheshire	120	73.3	63.5	14.1	8.3
Cleveland	157	71.5	59.5	13.2	6.8
Cornwall	120	74.6	64.3	15.0	9.0
Cumbria	115	72.8	63.6	14.1	8.5
Derbyshire	121	73.1	63.3	14.0	8.1
Devon	111	74.4	64.9	15.1	9.4
Dorset	101	75.2	66.2	15.7	10.0
Durham	166	72.0	59.1	13.3	6.6
East Sussex	106	74.3	65.2	15.3	9.6
Essex	101	74.6	65.8	14.8	9.1
Gloucestershire	97	74.5	66.2	14.9	9.6
Hampshire	97	74.5	66.1	14.9	9.4
Hereford & Worcester	101	74.4	65.8	14.5	9.2
Hertfordshire	89	75.1	67.3	15.0	9.6
Humberside	121	73.1	63.2	14.1	8.1
Isle of Wight	115	74.0	64.3	15.0	9.3
Kent	104	74.0	65.2	14.6	9.0
Lancashire	136	72.4	61.6	13.8	7.8
Leicestershire	102	74.1	65.4	14.8	9.3
Lincolnshire	113	73.7	64.3	14.5	9.0
Norfolk	105	74.7	65.6	15.2	9.5
North Yorkshire	99	73.6	65.3	14.4	9.0
Northamptonshire	130	73.1	62.6	13.7	7.9
Northumberland	104	74.2	65.3	14.7	9.0
Nottinghamshire	130	73.3	62.7	14.3	8.1
Oxfordshire	90	75.3	67.2	15.3	9.8
Shropshire	114	74.0	64.4	14.6	8.8
Somerset	100	74.9	66.2	15.3	9.8
Staffordshire	127	72.7	62.6	13.6	7.6
Suffolk	96	75.2	66.7	15.2	9.6
Surrey	83	75.7	68.2	15.5	10.3
Warwickshire	106	74.0	65.0	14.6	8.8
West Sussex	92	75.1	66.9	15.4	10.0
Wiltshire	95	74.5	66.3	14.8	9.4
Clwyd	139	73.6	62.1	14.5	8.0
Dyfed	146	73.6	61.6	14.4	8.2
Gwent	163	72.9	59.8	13.9	6.9
Gwynedd	131	73.5	62.6	14.7	8.7
Mid Glamorgan	201	72.2	56.5	13.4	5.8
Powys	121	74.0	63.7	14.7	9.0
South Glamorgan	136	73.3	62.2	14.3	8.0
West Glamorgan	174	73.0	59.0	14.0	6.9

Table 7.4: continued

	Disability rate[1]	Expectation at birth		Expectation at 65	
	per 1000	Life	HLE	Life	HLE
Women					
City of London	175	80.3	67.3	n.a.	n.a.
Barking & Dagenhan	146	78.6	66.1	18.2	10.1
Barnet	117	80.3	69.8	18.9	11.2
Bexley	119	80.1	69.5	18.8	11.0
Brent	142	79.5	67.1	19.1	10.8
Bromley	112	80.9	70.5	19.6	11.7
Camden	139	79.0	67.0	18.7	10.6
Croydon	124	79.3	68.7	18.1	10.8
Ealing	137	79.1	67.4	18.1	10.5
Enfield	124	80.2	69.1	19.1	11.2
Greenwich	143	78.7	66.6	18.1	10.1
Hackney	184	77.2	62.4	17.6	8.8
Hammersmith & Fulham	141	78.2	66.3	18.7	10.7
Haringey	154	78.8	65.8	18.2	9.9
Harrow	118	81.2	70.1	19.7	11.5
Havering	122	80.0	69.3	18.4	10.7
Hillingdon	120	79.8	69.2	18.9	11.3
Hounslow	130	79.6	68.3	18.6	10.7
Islington	160	78.1	64.8	17.9	10.0
Kensington & Chelsea	115	80.1	69.8	19.1	12.0
Kingston upon Thames	108	80.2	70.6	18.8	11.6
Lambeth	153	77.9	65.2	18.2	10.1
Lewisham	148	78.6	66.2	18.0	10.0
Merton	121	80.0	69.2	19.3	11.3
Newham	167	78.1	64.3	17.7	9.2
Redbridge	130	79.7	68.3	18.5	10.5
Richmond upon Thames	106	80.7	71.0	19.1	11.9
Southwark	154	77.4	64.9	17.7	10.0
Sutton	116	80.0	69.5	19.2	11.5
Tower Hamlets	164	78.5	64.8	18.3	9.8
Waltham Forest	143	78.9	66.7	18.4	10.2
Wandsworth	142	78.2	66.5	17.4	9.8
City of Westminster	125	79.6	68.5	19.6	11.9
Bolton	161	77.2	64.4	17.2	8.9
Bury	150	77.8	65.7	17.0	9.0
Manchester	181	76.6	62.4	17.0	8.6
Oldham	161	76.9	64.3	16.6	8.7
Rochdale	166	76.7	63.7	16.8	8.6
Salford	172	76.6	63.2	16.9	8.6
Stockport	129	79.0	68.0	17.9	10.2
Tameside	158	77.4	64.8	17.2	8.9
Trafford	136	78.5	67.1	18.1	10.1
Wigan	174	77.5	63.6	16.7	8.5
Knowsley	182	77.3	62.8	17.0	8.6
Liverpool	171	76.8	63.4	16.9	9.0
St Helens	170	77.5	63.8	17.2	8.7
Sefton	143	78.9	66.9	18.0	10.1
Wirral	147	78.0	66.0	17.5	9.7
Barnsley	185	77.6	62.8	17.4	8.0
Doncaster	169	78.1	64.2	17.8	8.8
Rotherham	174	78.2	63.9	17.6	8.2
Sheffield	157	78.4	65.3	17.8	9.0
Gateshead	169	77.5	64.0	17.0	8.5
Newcastle upon Tyne	157	77.3	64.8	17.2	9.2
North Tyneside	155	77.6	65.2	17.0	9.1
South Tyneside	162	77.4	64.5	17.0	8.8
Sunderland	181	76.8	62.6	16.7	7.9
Birmingham	150	77.9	65.5	17.9	9.8

Table 7.4: continued

	Disability rate[1] per 1000	Expectation at birth		Expectation at 65	
		Life	HLE	Life	HLE
Women					
Coventry	143	78.3	66.3	18.0	10.1
Dudley	137	78.9	67.4	18.1	9.8
Sandwell	157	77.9	65.1	17.8	9.3
Solihull	122	80.1	69.1	19.2	11.1
Walsall	154	77.7	65.3	17.5	9.2
Wolverhampton	156	77.9	65.2	17.7	9.2
Bradford	147	77.7	65.8	17.5	9.6
Calderdale	141	77.8	66.2	17.7	9.7
Kirklees	140	78.2	66.6	17.6	9.7
Leeds	141	78.7	66.8	18.2	9.9
Wakefield	162	77.7	64.5	17.4	8.5
Avon	121	80.1	69.3	18.8	11.0
Bedfordshire	124	78.9	68.4	18.1	10.5
Berkshire	112	79.6	69.9	18.5	11.3
Buckinghamshire	116	79.9	69.7	18.5	10.8
Cambridgeshire	121	80.1	69.3	18.8	11.1
Cheshire	137	78.5	67.1	17.7	9.9
Cleveland	166	76.9	63.8	16.8	8.5
Cornwall	131	79.8	68.4	18.7	10.8
Cumbria	130	78.1	67.4	17.6	10.2
Derbyshire	142	78.6	66.8	17.7	9.5
Devon	124	80.2	69.1	19.0	11.3
Dorset	118	80.7	69.9	19.4	11.7
Durham	171	77.3	63.7	17.0	8.5
East Sussex	122	80.1	69.2	19.2	11.6
Essex	122	79.7	69.1	18.5	10.8
Gloucestershire	115	80.0	69.7	19.1	11.5
Hampshire	119	79.9	69.4	18.8	11.2
Hereford & Worcester	122	79.5	69.0	18.4	10.9
Hertfordshire	114	80.1	70.1	18.6	11.1
Humberside	140	78.7	66.9	18.0	9.7
Isle of Wight	125	80.0	69.0	18.8	11.3
Kent	122	79.5	68.9	18.4	10.8
Lancashire	153	77.9	65.4	17.5	9.4
Leicestershire	124	79.6	68.7	18.7	11.0
Lincolnshire	130	79.1	67.9	18.4	10.6
Norfolk	122	80.0	69.3	18.8	11.2
North Yorkshire	123	78.8	68.4	18.2	10.6
Northamptonshire	140	78.0	66.7	17.4	9.8
Northumberland	122	79.5	68.9	18.4	10.7
Nottinghamshire	144	78.8	66.7	18.0	9.8
Oxfordshire	111	80.4	70.3	19.1	11.5
Shropshire	130	79.5	68.2	18.4	10.5
Somerset	116	80.4	70.0	19.0	11.5
Staffordshire	148	78.3	66.1	17.6	9.3
Suffolk	116	80.1	69.8	18.8	11.2
Surrey	106	80.6	70.9	19.1	11.8
Warwickshire	127	79.0	68.2	18.2	10.4
West Sussex	111	80.4	70.4	19.1	11.7
Wiltshire	118	79.7	69.5	18.5	11.1
Clwyd	151	79.3	66.3	18.4	9.8
Dyfed	151	79.1	66.2	18.4	10.3
Gwent	174	78.5	64.1	17.6	8.8
Gwynedd	133	79.8	68.0	19.0	11.0
Mid Glamorgan	207	77.9	61.2	17.3	7.9
Powys	132	79.5	68.1	18.6	11.0
South Glamorgan	147	79.1	66.6	18.3	10.0
West Glamorgan	185	78.8	63.3	18.1	8.7

[1] Age standardised

Access to services

The argument is that health is in part the consequence of health services and access to such services is impeded in rural areas where mobility may be a problem. Population sparsity has been measured by area in hectares divided by 1991 corrected mid-year population. Counties with more hectares than population include Cumbria, Lincolnshire, North Yorkshire, Dyfed, Gwynedd and Powys. .

Ethnic group

Mortality differentials between immigrants and the indigenous population have previously been reported (Marmot et al, 1984; Balarajan and Bulusu, 1989). The 1991 Census provides direct evidence of health, and Table 7.5 shows from the age-standardised LLI rates that most ethnic minorities experience above average limiting long-standing illness. The size of ethnic minorities is measured by the percentage of all persons self-describing as other than 'White', as tabulated in SAS Table 6.

Table 7.5   Age standardised disability rate by ethnic group, England and Wales, 1991

Ethnic group	Males	Females
White	117	127
Black-Caribbean	132	171
Black-African	131	161
Black-Other	141	166
Indian	132	171
Pakistani	168	186
Bangladeshi	175	160
Chinese	85	101
Other Asian	106	133
Other groups	121	153
Overall	118	129

Source: Reanalysis of 1991 Census Limiting Long-term Illness volume, Table 3, England and Wales, residents in households.

Retirement migration

Some areas are specially attractive as retirement areas, and people who are able to migrate on retirement to them are known to be fairly affluent (i.e. owner occupiers) and relatively healthy. The retirement migration potential of areas is measured by the proportion (per mille) of all residents who are people of pensionable age who have moved into the county within the last year, from SAS Table 15. (Moves within a county, or within London, are not counted.) Counties where at least 3 residents per 1,000 fall into this category include Dorset, Isle of Wight, Lincolnshire, Somerset, East Sussex, West Sussex, Powys.

The relative significance of these factors has been investigated by multiple regression in which the dependent variable is male and female HE at birth for each area as shown in Table 7.4. (City of London was excluded from this analysis leaving 115 areas.) Table 7.6 shows the results of these analyses. 83 per cent of the variation (R^2) in both male and female HE can be explained. In effect this implies that almost all the variation between local areas is accounted for by this set of factors. All the factors included are significant

in their impact on HE, though sparsity only marginally so[5]. The unemployment rate is the most significant for men, retirement migration rate for women.

High unemployment, low social class, high sparsity all reduce HE. HE is higher in areas of retirement migration. But a surprise is that, *after* taking these other factors into account, HE is actually slightly higher in areas with substantial ethnic minorities. Such areas where HE is higher than expected (though still a long way below average) include Tower Hamlets, Haringey, Hackney for men, Tower Hamlets and Southwark for women.

7.5 Health expectancy for ethnic minorities

The following analysis is more speculative, but has been included in the report because of the interest of its findings.

HE cannot be measured unless age specific mortality rates are available by ethnic group. Death certificates show country of birth, and this has been used as a proxy for ethnic group in order to analyse mortality patterns in the period around the 1981 Census (Balarajan and Bulusu, 1989). On the whole this has proved reassuring that mortality rates among immigrants are mostly similar to or even below that of the indigenous population, though they were rather above average among immigrants from Africa as was infant mortality among mothers from Pakistan (Balarajan and Raleigh, 1989).

Country of birth is not an entirely satisfactory proxy for ethnicity, and is becoming less so, as immigration decreases and ethnic groups increasingly comprise the descendents of the immigrants who entered the UK earlier this century. Moreover an average mortality rate is at odds with the social class composition of ethnic groups descended from new Commonwealth immigrants, among whom low social class occupations and unemployment is well above average. (GB unemployment rates for economically active males in the 1991 Census were 13.4 per cent for Whites, 25.2 per cent for other ethnic groups). In the US large variations have been found: life expectancy of Blacks is around 8 years less than that of Whites (NCHS, 1991), and infant mortality more than twice as high.

Immigrants are a particularly healthy group, if only because health is a condition of entry, and so if this level of health persisted for some time after immigration it would explain why earlier data might over-estimate the long-run health situation of ethnic groups. Clearly, an alternative approach is now desirable.

---

[5]The regression coefficients in Table 7.6 show the predicted effect of each factor on healthy life expectancy. For example, for males each one percent increase in the number of people in social class IV or V in an area, will be associated with a fall of 0.20 years in healthy life expectancies. The beta coefficients, also known as path coefficients, show the change in standard deviations of HE associated from a one standard deviation increase in each factor. This provides some guidance as to the relative causative importance of each factor.

Table 7.6: **Regression analysis of factors affecting the mean HLE rates of local authority areas in England and Wales**

Factor	Regression coefficient	Standard error	Beta coefficient	Significance level
HLE for Males				
Social Class IV and V (%)	-0.20	0.04	-0.29	< 1%
Unemployment Rate (%) Population Sparsity	-0.37	0.05	-0.53	< 1%
Retirement Migration (per ml)	-0.78	0.27	-0.14	< 1%
Non-white Population (%)	1.29	0.19	0.39	< 1%
	0.08	0.02	0.27	< 1%
Constant	68.45			
R^2	0.827			
HLE for Females				
Social Class IV and V (%)	-0.20	0.03	-0.34	< 1%
Unemployment Rate (%) Population Sparsity	-0.24	0.04	-0.40	< 1%
Retirement Migration (per ml)	-0.52	0.23	-0.11	< 1%
Non-white Population (%)	1.34	0.16	0.46	< 1%
	0.05	0.01	0.22	< 1%
Constant	70.97			
R^2	0.825			

Based on 115 local government areas of England and Wales. See text for detailed definition of variables.

Table 7.7: **Synthetic estimates of mortality rates among wards in London**

	0-34	35-54	55-64	65-74	75+
Men					
Black	19	43	121	439	1962
	(2)	(11)	(18)	(67)	(452)
Indian sub-continent	9	37	159	371	840
	(1)	(4)	(15)	(52)	(252)
Others, unemployed HOH	37	236	647	984	1558
	(6)	(19)	(49)	(88)	(217)
Others, social class IV or V	7	58	147	520	1251
	(5)	(14)	(40)	(72)	(181)
Others, remainder	4	11	55	246	938
	(1)	(1)	(4)	(8)	(20)
Women					
Black	7	22	105	300	1184
	(1)	(3)	(14)	(61)	(780)
Indian sub-continent	4	13	74	306	1111
	(1)	(3)	(14)	(49)	(531)
Others, unemployed HOH	13	56	226	517	1587
	(4)	(11)	(32)	(56)	(233)
Others, social class IV or V	9	18	115	280	556
	(3)	(8)	(26)	(46)	(193)
Others, remainder	2	12	46	142	816
	(0)	(1)	(3)	(5)	(21)

Mortality rates are per 10,000 population. Figures in brackets are standard errors of estimates. For derivation see section 7.5

Some studies of ethnicity and health, e.g. Knight et al (1993), have based their inferences on the geographical distribution of both disease and ethnic groups. The link with geography allows us to consider 'synthetic' approaches to estimating mortality rates. The following analysis is based on 1991 death rates (three-year average) for the 755 wards in Greater London with a population exceeding 1000[6].

The assumption of the synthetic approach is that overall mortality rate of a ward will be determined by the representation in it of each of a number of population subgroups, each of which has its own fixed mortality rate. By turning the equation around, it becomes possible to infer the mortality rate of each subgroup from the overall mortality rate of each ward.

Mathematically, if there are (for men and women separately)

- $j = 1,..,J$ subgroups; $k = 1,..,K$ areas;
- P_{ijk} is the number of residents in age group i, subgroup j, and area k;
- m_{ij} denotes the unknown age specific mortality rates for subgroup j;
- D_{ik} is the number of deaths (all subgroups) in area a;

Then:

$$D_{i,k} = \sum_{j=1}^{J} m_{i,j} \times P_{i,j,k}$$

And given a sufficiently large number of areas, 'J', the m_{ij} can be estimated by least squares.

This approach has been applied to wards of London to estimate mortality rates for ethnic groups[6]. However, it would be a mistake to assume that the mortality rate of a ward is simply reflected by its ethnic composition. In section 7.4 we showed that other factors affect local mortality rates. Wards with large ethnic minority groups are also areas in which the White population is typically of lower social class and therefore has a higher than average mortality rate. Allowance must be made for the social class of Whites, otherwise the mortality rates of ethnic minorities will be overestimated.

For this analysis the population of each ward has therefore been divided into five subgroups:

- Black ethnic groups;
- Indian sub-continent ethnic groups;
- Others (mainly Whites) with economically active unemployed HOH;
- Others (mainly Whites) in social class IV or V, (excluding those in the previous group);
- Others (mainly Whites in social classes I - III)[7].

Broad ethnic groups have been used because of the small numbers in minority groups in many wards. Very coarse age groups have been used: 0 - 34, 35 - 54, 55 - 64, 65 - 74, 75+, because of the small numbers of deaths per ward in

each age group. The analysis is undertaken for each age group and sex separately, and the resulting estimates of mortality rates are shown in Table 7.7. It should be noted that the standard errors of estimates relating to older age-groups for ethnic minorities are in some cases rather high. Little attention should be paid to mortality relativities among the social class subgroups of the 'Other' ethnic group owing to the approximation described in footnote 7. These three groups are combined into one in Table 7.8, which shows life expectancies derived from these estimated age-specific mortality rates.

The limiting long-standing illness rates for ethnic groups across London are obtained from the *1991 Census Limiting Long-term Illness* report, Table 6. This does not show age-specific rates, but these have been estimated by applying the overall rate for each ethnic group in London to the national age breakdown shown in Table 3 in the report, after adjusting for the slightly different age structure[8]. Finally health expectancy for each ethnic group in London has been calculated by Sullivan's method.

Table 7.8 shows that Black men can expect four years less HE than White (and other) men, and Black women can expect six years less. Those of Indian sub-continent descent also have a lower HE than Whites, though the differences are rather less, 2.5 years for men and 5 years for women. Most of the difference in health expectancy is accounted for by differences in life expectancy. It is possible that this might reflect differences between ethnic groups in willingness to report oneself as having limiting long-standing illness. These results imply that these ethnic minorities can expect fewer years of good health than can Whites.

We remind the reader that the synthetic estimation approach is speculative, and with large standard deviations it would be unwise to read too much into the exact magnitudes of these results. However the analysis does provide evidence that people from ethnic minorities have lower than average healthy life expectancy. This is probably largely if not entirely explained by the difference in social class composition of the White and non-White populations.

---

[6]We are grateful to John Charlton of OPCS for supplying age/sex specific death statistics for 1990-1992 by ward. The link between ethnic composition and ward mortality rates is evident from the following observation. Those wards with substantial ethnic minorities also have high death rates for their age composition. This may be illustrated in relation to people under 35. Of the 100 wards in which one in five (or more) of the residents are described as Black Caribbean, Black African, or Black, 44 per cent had a death rate in this age group exceeding 1 per 1000, compared with only 16 per cent of the remaining 655 wards.

[7]Attention should be drawn to two problems in using the Census. First, under-enumeration of the population means that death rates calculated on the basis of the Census population are over-estimates. If wards with large numbers of people from ethnic minorities are also wards with the greatest under-enumeration, the methodology given may tend to exaggerate the estimated death rates for ethnic minorities more than for other groups. However it has not been possible to adjust for this. Second, census small area statistics do not give a breakdown of numbers of residents by age x ethnic group x social class/employment status of HOH. This breakdown has been approximated by applying the ward's adult unemployment rate among the economically active in 'other' ethnic groups (local base statistics table L09) to the numbers of 'others' in each age/sex group in the ward; then by applying the proportion of 'other' adults in social class IV and V (from LBS table 93) to the remainder in each age /sex group in the ward.

Table 7.8: **Synthetic estimates of life expectancy and HLE by age, sex and ethnic group**

Age group	Mortality rate (per 10000)	Life table (years)	Life expectancy %	LLI rate (years)	HLE
Black men					
0-34	19	1,000	68.6	4.79	59.6
35-54	43	9,356	37.1	9.80	29.2
55-64	121	8,580	19.6	25.41	13.0
65-74	439	7,600	11.5	37.77	6.7
75+	1,962	4,861	5.1	49.51	2.6
Indian sub-continent men					
0-34	9	1,000	74.3	3.40	62.2
35-54	37	9,702	41.0	12.83	29.8
55-64	59	9,004	23.4	35.23	14.0
65-74	371	7,680	16.6	40.73	9.4
75+	840	5,276	11.9	46.47	6.4
White & other men					
0-34	9	1,000	73.2	3.25	63.7
35-54	39	9,697	39.9	8.76	31.3
55-64	138	8,977	22.4	25.60	14.9
65-74	374	7,819	14.9	34.12	9.1
75+	1,054	5,355	9.5	45.74	5.2
Black women					
0-34	7	1,000	75.1	4.29	62.4
35-54	22	9,765	41.5	12.67	30.0
55-64	105	9,336	22.9	31.86	13.5
65-74	300	8,401	14.9	42.28	7.8
75+	1,185	6,206	8.4	54.86	3.8
Indian sub-continent women					
0-34	4	10,000	77.1	2.98	63.5
35-54	13	9,864	42.9	13.77	30.2
55-64	74	9,604	23.8	36.47	13.5
65-74	306	8,919	15.3	43.31	8.0
75+	1,111	6,552	9.0	53.60	4.2
White & other women					
0-34	5	1,000	80.1	2.88	68.6
35-54	18	9,842	46.1	8.46	35.4
55-64	77	9,499	27.4	20.49	18.1
65-74	207	8,793	19.2	30.81	11.3
75+	803	7,146	12.5	50.56	6.2

[8]The limiting long-standing illness rate for age group 'i', ethnic group 'j', in London, is estimated by:

$$d'_{i,j} = \frac{L_{i,j}}{P_{i,j}} \div \frac{L'_j}{\sum_i \frac{L_{i,j}}{P_{i,j}} \cdot P'_{i,j}}$$

where $L_{i,j}$ denotes the number nationally who are LLI; $P_{i,j}$ denotes the national population; L'_j denotes the number who are LLI in London, and $P'_{i,j}$ denotes the population in London.

8 Gains in healthy life expectancy from the elimination of specified diseases

Measures of the impact of various diseases are important for setting priorities in disease prevention. Impact is a combination of the incidence, combined with duration, severity, long-term health consequences and mortality for individuals, associated with each particular disease. This chapter demonstrates a method of bringing these together in a measure of expected life years lost as a consequence of each disease. The method extends the cause-deleted life table approach (Tsai et al, 1978) to incorporate gains in disability-free life expectancy theoretically arising from the complete elimination of a disease.

8.1 Methodology

The approach used is to combine a cause deleted measure of life expectancy using conventional life table methods with a cause deleted population disablement rate. While several techniques have been proposed, as far as possible we have followed the approach recently used by Mathers (1992) with the Australian Bureau of Statistics 1988 Survey of Disability and Handicap. With this method

- all deaths associated with a particular cause are simply ignored in calculating the age-specific mortality rates q_x which are used for life table calculations;

- all disablements from the same cause are ignored in calculating the age-specific disablement rates which form the basis for estimating healthy life expectancy.

This approach assumes that causes of death and disablement are subjected to independent competing risks. It is not entirely realistic since such causes are undoubtedly related and the removal of one cause would affect the probability of other causes. Moreover, no allowance is made for the possibility of multiple causes of death or disablement. Where more than one cause is reported, death or disablement must be attributed uniquely to one of these causes.

For the present study data relate to the period around 1986, for England and Wales. Deaths were classified into 30 principal underlying causes, and (for comparability with Mathers) further simplified into the 17 ICD9 chapters. The information, abstracted from OPCS series DH2, consists of the average annual number of deaths, by each principal cause, by age and sex, over the three years 1985-7. Contributory causes of death are ignored. The total number of deaths (all causes) are shown in Table 8.1; and the number of deaths by principal cause in Table 8.2.

Numbers of disabled persons circa 1986 by cause of disability was obtained by reanalysis of the four parts of the OPCS Disability Survey. This analysis required that all individuals be classified according to principle cause of disability, corresponding to the ICD9 chapters used with death reports. This required a reclassification of all complaints reported by respondents in the disability survey into the most likely ICD9 chapter[9].

The next stage is to identify principal cause of disability. This is not straightforward because both death and disability may have a number of contributory causes, and in practice it is never possible to say whether death would have occurred if one of a number of factors is removed, or what level disability might have been expected. This problem applies to both the calculation of cause-deleted life expectancy and HE, but is worse for the latter because multiple conditions are so common. Up to ten separate health conditions were cited in the Disability Surveys and 78 per cent of all disabled people (after reweighting) cited multiple health conditions as contributing to disability. We have considered four possible approaches to this problem.

- Treat each health condition entirely separately. This approach can be used for estimating 'condition'-free life expectancy which is calculated like HE but concentrating on a single disabling health condition. Cause-deleted life expectancy and HE can be calculated by calculating age-specific death and disablement rates that ignore all deaths and disablements occurring to individuals for whom this condition was present. This approach is however very unrealistic in that the particular condition may have been a minor problem and would have made little difference to the individual's health. The resulting estimates of improvement to life expectancy would grossly overestimate the actual effect of deleting any cause, and in particular would overstate the impact of minor conditions.

- Classify each individual according to the first-mentioned condition as probably being the one of greatest concern, and calculate cause-deleted life expectancy on this basis. This is the approach in effect used by Mathers. This approach also overestimates the actual effect of deleting one cause, since in reality many people are disabled by a combination of conditions, though it will give a fairer picture of the relative significance of each cause.

---

[9]This was done at the time when the surveys were originally coded, but due to some oddities, e.g. the classification of many injuries along with disease, has been recoded for the present exercise. All four surveys needed different reclassification. Full details of this recoding are too lengthy to include here but are available from the authors.

Table 8.1:   Population, deaths and disablement (all causes) summary

	Men			Women		
	Population	Deaths	Disabled	Population	Deaths	Disabled
< 1	336,100	2,278	612	318,800	1,651	951
1- 4	1,296,100	596	33,695	1,232,200	492	22,356
5- 9	1,553,300	321	72,123	1,471,300	248	43,278
10-14	1,651,900	429	75,297	1,561,600	275	45,786
15-19	2,004,500	1,397	45,146	1,906,700	540	38,230
20-24	2,130,400	1,765	54,102	2,072,200	637	53,984
25-29	1,877,000	1,470	42,862	1,847,000	676	66,952
30-34	1,683,000	1,621	54,673	1,658,300	947	70,193
35-39	1,851,200	2,367	65,199	1,848,700	1,576	87,338
40-44	1,593,200	3,422	74,876	1,570,100	2,259	99,446
45-49	1,394,200	5,296	86,397	1,382,000	3,419	105,301
50-54	1,334,000	9,000	124,411	1,332,700	5,463	133,655
55-59	1,328,900	16,121	199,123	1,374,000	9,537	212,233
60-64	1,299,400	27,448	271,777	1,415,100	16,612	237,301
65-69	1,071,500	35,662	291,199	1,279,300	22,822	313,068
70-74	897,200	48,389	298,868	1,210,100	35,012	397,059
75-79	625,900	53,426	275,371	1,014,000	49,048	481,256
80-84	325,900	42,448	189,778	688,600	56,924	404,011
85+	149,900	31,997	106,115	489,000	83,357	340,007
Total	24,403,600	285,454	2,361,624	25,671,700	291,498	3,152,405

Source: Population is OPCS mid-year estimate England and Wales, 1986. Deaths are the average of the three years 1985-7, all causes combined (supplied by OPCS). Numbers disabled have been calculated from reanalysis of the disability survey. (The numbers correspond to the figures shown in OPCS Disability Report 1, table 3.6, and Report 3, table 3.5, total all severities, private households and communal establishments combined, but are for England and Wales only and use a more detailed age breakdown.)

- Calculate cause-deleted life expectancy by deleting only those individuals for whom the condition is the sole cause of death or disablement. This approach will give a very low estimate of the effect of deleting any one cause, but begs for the effect of multiple causes to be investigated since the effect of deleting a combination of causes will invariably be greater than the sums of their individual effects.

- Develop a statistical model that predicts the probability of death from any combination of causes, and the level of disability expected to result from any combination of causes. Then the reduction in expected deaths and the number of people above a given disability threshold may be predicted for any combination of causes from the model. This is in principle the most satisfactory approach. However, in practice fitting this model is difficult specially as with the available data source, the OPCS Disability Surveys, we know nothing about the incidence of conditions in the undisabled population.

In view of these problems the present analysis is confined to the second of these approaches, and we have chosen the threshold of all disability levels as defined by the Disability Survey (Martin et al, 1988, chapter 2). Table 8.1 shows the estimated number of people in England and Wales with any disability by age and sex, and Table 8.2 by principal cause calculated on this basis.

8.2 Findings

Tables 8.3 and 8.4 show, at birth and at age 65 respectively, the extra years that would be lived, and the extra years that

would be lived in good health; if each one in turn of the principal causes of ill-health and death were eliminated. This saving is calculated by comparing the cause-deleted life expectancy, and health expectancy, with the undeleted expectancies shown in the final row of the tables.

The gain from the elimination of any one condition is surprisingly small: it would be smaller still if multiple causes of disability/death had been taken into account. Elimination of circulatory diseases would lead to the greatest gain in life expectancy and hence, though to a slightly lesser degree, in health expectancy (Figure 8.1). Elimination of musculo-skeletal disorders would lead to the next greatest gain in health expectancy, at least for women, though it is an insignificant cause of premature death. Diseases of the nervous system and mental disorders are also much more significant to health expectancy than they are to total life expectancy.

The pattern of these results correspond closely to those given by Mathers (1992, Figures 4 and 5); with the exception of gains in healthy life due to the elimination of injury, which were estimated as 6.1 years for men and 2.8 years for women, from birth. This difference is undoubtedly due to the way in which the Australian survey was handled: respondents were first asked if their disability was due to accident or illness, before cause was investigated in detail. In the British survey, by contrast, self-reported causes were coded in such a way that it is not always possible to distinguish injury from illness.

Table 8.2: Deaths and disabilities by principal cause

(A) Twenty-nine conditions	Deaths	People disabled
1 Infectious and parasitic	2,409	39,807
2 Neoplasms of digestive organs	40,799	10,953
3 Neoplasms of respiratory and intrathorgans	36,930	8,498
4 Neoplasms of reproductive organs	35,624	15,430
5 Neoplasms; other	28,271	27,014
6 Endocrine and metabolic	9,922	144,466
7 Depression	240	130,756
8 Senile dementia	9,498	42,148
9 Other mental illness	2,548	330,955
10 Eye complaints	10	328,051
11 Ear complaints	38	539,829
12 Nervous system, excl. eye & ear	11,136	307,439
13 Coronary heart/artery disease	159,002	320,077
14 Circulatory system; other	48,578	367,066
15 Bronchitis & emphysema	29,488	209,754
16 Pneumonia	27,199	0
17 Respiratory; other	4,891	250,938
18 Digestive system	17,930	148,683
19 Genito-urinary system	7,545	99,185
20 Skin disease or disorder	716	25,416
21 Arthritis, rheumatoid and osteo-arthritis	3,203	1,168,935
22 Back problems	234	113,102
23 Musculoskeletal; other	1,927	195,403
24 Congenital	3,097	28,815
25 Cerebrovascular disease	71,374	195,429
26 All other blood organs	2,370	18,610
27 Injury, poisonings	18,529	293,286
28 Old age	1,614	66,640
29 Other ill-defined conditions	1,832	87,340

(B) ICD chapters	Deaths	People disabled
1 Infectious diseases	2,409	39,810
2 Neoplasms	141,623	61,895
3 Endocrinal, metabolic	9,922	144,468
4 Blood organs	2,370	18,611
5 Mental disorders	12,286	503,861
6 Nervous system	11,183	1,175,320
7 Circulatory system	278,955	882,572
8 Respiratory	61,578	460,695
9 Digestive	17,930	148,683
10 Genito-urinary	7,545	99,182
11 Pregnancy	0	0
12 Skin	716	25,416
13 Musculoskeletal system	5,364	1,477,441
14/15 Congenital (& natal)	3,097	28,815
16 Signs and symptoms	3,446	153,979
17 Injuries, poisonings	18,529	293,288

For sources, see notes to table 8.1. This is a reanalysis of the Disability Surveys including children and people in communal establishments.

Table 8.3: Life years and healthy life years saved from birth by the elimination of specific causes

Cause	Men				Women			
	Life expt	Life saved	HLE expt	HLE saved	Life expt	Life saved	HLE expt	HLE saved
(A) Twenty-nine conditions								
1 Infectious and parasitic	72.48	0.08	64.76	0.12	78.20	0.07	68.06	0.12
2 Neoplasms of digestive organs	73.25	0.85	65.16	0.52	78.94	0.81	68.38	0.43
3 Neoplasms of respiratory and inthraorgans	73.45	1.05	65.26	0.62	78.63	0.50	68.23	0.29
4 Neoplasms of reproductive organs	72.80	0.40	64.85	0.21	79.45	1.33	68.78	0.84
5 Neoplasms; other	73.09	0.69	65.14	0.50	78.83	0.70	68.40	0.45
6 Endocrine and metabolic	72.58	0.18	64.94	0.30	78.36	0.23	68.35	0.41
7 Depression	72.40	0.00	64.77	0.13	78.13	0.00	68.21	0.27
8 Senile dementia	72.48	0.08	64.71	0.07	78.31	0.18	68.13	0.18
9 Other mental illness	72.46	0.05	65.14	0.50	78.18	0.05	68.49	0.55
10 Eye complaints	72.40	0.00	65.07	0.43	78.13	0.00	68.62	0.68
11 Ear complaints	72.40	0.00	65.56	0.92	78.13	0.00	68.78	0.83
12 Nervous system, excl. eye, ear	72.66	0.26	65.26	0.62	78.40	0.27	68.60	0.66
13 Coronary heart/artery disease	76.48	4.07	67.56	2.92	80.94	2.81	69.75	1.80
14 Circulatory system; other	73.12	0.72	65.53	0.89	79.12	0.99	69.13	1.19
15 Bronchitis & emphysema	73.06	0.66	65.49	0.85	78.52	0.39	68.36	0.42
16 Pneumonia	72.72	0.31	64.79	0.15	78.67	0.54	68.15	0.21
17 Respiratory; other	72.51	0.11	65.16	0.52	78.23	0.10	68.37	0.42
18 Digestive system	72.70	0.30	65.03	0.39	78.52	0.39	68.41	0.46
19 Genito-urinary system	72.51	0.11	64.86	0.22	78.25	0.13	68.15	0.21
20 Skin disease or disorder	72.41	0.01	64.69	0.05	78.14	0.02	67.99	0.04
21 Arthritis, rheumatoid and osteoarthritis	72.42	0.02	65.66	1.02	78.22	0.09	70.86	2.91
22 Back problems	72.40	0.00	64.81	0.17	78.13	0.00	68.14	0.20
23 Musculoskeletal; other	72.41	0.01	64.93	0.29	78.17	0.04	68.32	0.38
24 Congenital	72.69	0.29	64.93	0.29	78.40	0.27	68.22	0.27
25 Cerebrovascular disease	73.32	0.92	65.45	0.81	79.73	1.60	68.98	1.03
26 All other blood organs	72.44	0.04	64.69	0.05	78.18	0.05	68.00	0.06
27 Injury, poisonings	73.38	0.98	65.97	1.33	78.64	0.51	68.71	0.77
28 Old age	72.41	0.01	64.71	0.07	78.16	0.03	68.15	0.21
29 Other symptoms, signs	72.59	0.19	64.94	0.30	78.27	0.14	68.20	0.26
Undeleted	72.40	0.00	64.64	0.00	78.13	0.00	67.94	0.00
ICD chapters								
1 Infectious diseases	72.48	0.08	64.76	0.12	78.20	0.07	68.06	0.12
2 Neoplasms	75.73	3.33	66.64	2.00	81.72	3.60	70.08	2.14
3 Endocrinal, metabolic	72.58	0.18	64.94	0.30	78.36	0.23	68.35	0.41
4 Blood organs	72.44	0.04	64.69	0.05	78.18	0.05	68.00	0.06
5 Mental disorders	72.53	0.13	65.34	0.70	78.37	0.24	68.94	1.00
6 Nervous system	72.66	0.26	66.63	1.99	78.40	0.27	70.13	2.19
7 Circulatory system	79.79	7.39	70.35	5.71	86.38	8.26	73.55	5.61
8 Respiratory	73.56	1.16	66.24	1.60	79.21	1.08	69.03	1.08
9 Digestive	72.70	0.30	65.03	0.39	78.52	0.39	68.41	0.46
10 Genito-urinary	72.51	0.11	64.86	0.22	78.25	0.13	68.15	0.21
11 Pregnancy	72.40	0.00	64.64	0.00	78.13	0.00	67.94	0.00
12 Skin	72.41	0.01	64.69	0.05	78.14	0.02	67.99	0.04
13 Musculoskeletal system	72.44	0.04	66.11	1.47	78.26	0.13	71.45	3.50
14/15 Congenital (& natal)	72.69	0.29	64.93	0.29	78.40	0.27	68.22	0.27
16 Signs and symptoms	72.60	0.19	65.01	0.37	78.30	0.17	68.41	0.47
17 Injuries, poisonings	73.38	0.98	65.97	1.33	78.64	0.51	68.71	0.77
Undeleted	72.40	0.00	64.64	0.00	78.13	0.00	67.94	0.00

Table 8.4: Life years and healthy life years saved from 65 by the elimination of specific causes

Cause	Men				Women			
	Life expt	Life saved	HLE expt	HLE saved	Life expt	Life saved	HLE expt	HLE saved
(A) Twenty-nine conditions								
1 Infectious and parasitic	13.60	0.02	8.32	0.04	17.57	0.03	10.16	0.03
2 Neoplasms of digestive organs	14.17	0.59	8.59	0.30	18.13	0.58	10.39	0.26
3 Neoplasms of respiratory and inthraorgans	14.33	0.75	8.66	0.37	17.85	0.30	10.27	0.14
4 Neoplasms of reproductive organs	13.93	0.36	8.45	0.16	18.13	0.58	10.42	0.29
5 Neoplasms; other	13.91	0.34	8.48	0.19	17.92	0.37	10.31	0.18
6 Endocrine and metabolic	13.69	0.11	8.49	0.21	17.72	0.17	10.42	0.29
7 Depression	13.58	0.00	8.32	0.03	17.55	0.00	10.17	0.04
8 Senile dementia	13.67	0.09	8.37	0.08	17.75	0.20	10.33	0.20
9 Other mental illness	13.60	0.02	8.34	0.05	17.58	0.04	10.25	0.13
10 Eye complaints	13.58	0.00	8.68	0.40	17.54	0.00	10.76	0.63
11 Ear complaints	13.58	0.00	8.91	0.62	17.55	0.00	10.68	0.55
12 Nervous system, excl. eye, ear	13.71	0.13	8.51	0.22	17.70	0.16	10.34	0.21
13 Coronary heart/artery disease	16.54	2.96	10.19	1.90	20.17	2.63	11.68	1.55
14 Circulatory system; other	14.19	0.62	8.95	0.66	18.49	0.94	11.15	1.03
15 Bronchitis & emphysema	14.21	0.63	9.06	0.78	17.84	0.29	10.42	0.30
16 Pneumonia	13.89	0.31	8.40	0.12	18.10	0.56	10.32	0.19
17 Respiratory; other	13.65	0.07	8.63	0.34	17.61	0.07	10.32	0.20
18 Digestive system	13.77	0.19	8.53	0.24	17.85	0.30	10.45	0.33
19 Genito-urinary system	13.69	0.11	8.44	0.15	17.66	0.11	10.22	0.10
20 Skin disease or disorder	13.58	0.01	8.31	0.02	17.56	0.02	10.15	0.02
21 Arthritis, rheumatoid and osteoarthritis	13.60	0.02	9.12	0.83	17.62	0.07	12.65	2.52
22 Back problems	13.58	0.00	8.34	0.05	17.55	0.00	10.21	0.09
23 Musculoskeletal; other	13.59	0.01	8.51	0.22	17.59	0.04	10.42	0.29
24 Congenital	13.58	0.01	8.29	0.01	17.55	0.01	10.15	0.02
25 Cerebrovascular disease	14.45	0.87	9.00	0.71	19.11	1.57	11.06	0.93
26 All other blood organs	13.60	0.03	8.32	0.03	17.59	0.04	10.17	0.04
27 Injury, poisonings	13.68	0.11	8.62	0.33	17.69	0.15	10.47	0.34
28 Old age	13.59	0.01	8.37	0.09	17.58	0.04	10.37	0.24
29 Other symptoms, signs	13.58	0.00	8.35	0.06	17.55	0.01	10.21	0.09
Undeleted	13.58	0.00	8.29	0.00	17.54	0.00	10.13	0.00
ICD chapters								
1 Infectious diseases	13.60	0.02	8.32	0.04	17.57	0.03	10.16	0.03
2 Neoplasms	15.87	2.29	9.43	1.14	19.53	1.99	11.07	0.94
3 Endocrinal, metabolic	13.69	0.11	8.49	0.21	17.72	0.17	10.42	0.29
4 Blood organs	13.60	0.03	8.32	0.03	17.59	0.04	10.17	0.04
5 Mental disorders	13.70	0.12	8.46	0.17	17.79	0.25	10.50	0.38
6 Nervous system	13.71	0.13	9.54	1.25	17.70	0.16	11.54	1.42
7 Circulatory system	19.70	6.13	12.59	4.31	25.73	8.19	15.31	5.18
8 Respiratory	14.68	1.10	9.62	1.33	18.52	0.97	10.84	0.71
9 Digestive	13.77	0.19	8.53	0.24	17.85	0.30	10.45	0.33
10 Genito-urinary	13.69	0.11	8.43	0.15	17.66	0.11	10.22	0.10
11 Pregnancy	13.58	0.00	8.29	0.00	17.54	0.00	10.13	0.00
12 Skin	13.58	0.01	8.31	0.02	17.56	0.02	10.15	0.02
13 Musculoskeletal system	13.62	0.04	9.39	1.11	17.67	0.12	13.03	2.91
14/15 Congenital (& natal)	13.58	0.01	8.29	0.01	17.55	0.01	10.15	0.02
16 Signs and symptoms	13.59	0.01	8.44	0.15	17.59	0.04	10.46	0.33
17 Injuries, poisonings	13.68	0.11	8.62	0.33	17.69	0.15	10.47	0.34
Undeleted	13.58	0.00	8.29	0.00	17.54	0.00	10.13	0.00

Figure 8.1: Increase in health expectancies at birth, after the elimination of major disease groups, Australia 1988 and UK 1986

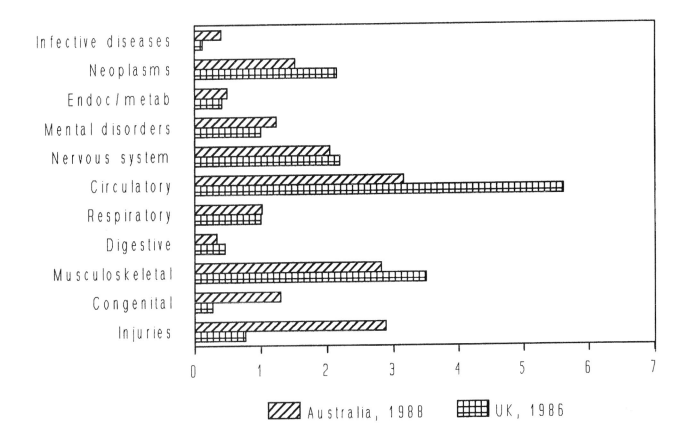

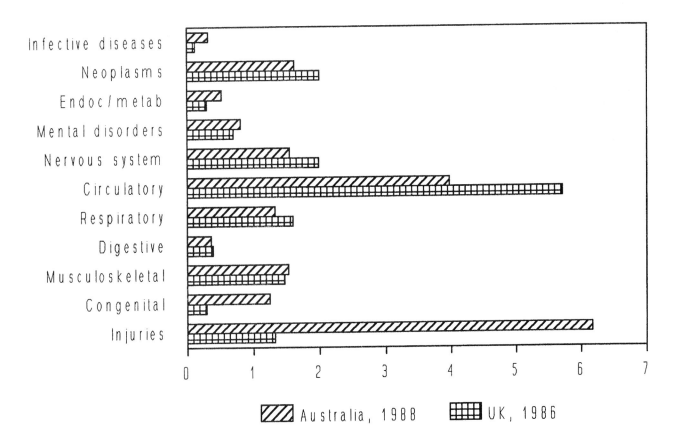

9 Health expectancies under differing definitions of health: methodology

The health expectancies shown in chapters 6 to 8 were all estimated from national cross-sectional data by Sullivan's method, because no suitable longitudinal data exist at the national level. In the following two chapters we compare health expectancies calculated from both cross-sectional and longitudinal data generated by the same local studies, using a variety of definitions of health. These health expectancies are the first to use UK longitudinal data.

Two longitudinal studies provide the basis for chapters 10 and 11, both drawn from defined populations, with high response rates and first follow-up at around four years. Each study had all subjects flagged at the National Health Service Central Registry (NHSCR) at Southport to provide details of death. All mortality data were complete up to 1st January 1992. This chapter provides descriptions of the studies and comparisons of demographic characteristics both between the studies and with Census data, the latter to establish the generalisation of inferences made from the data to wider populations.

9.1 The Nottingham Longitudinal Study of Activity and Aging (NLSAA)

The Nottingham Longitudinal Study of Activity and Aging (NLSAA) is an age-stratified sample of elderly people aged 65 years and over from the Nottinghamshire FPC lists, the areas sampled being chosen to have similar age, sex, ethnic and social class distributions to England and Wales (1981 census). The baseline interview on 1,042 people living in the community took place in 1985 with the follow-up interview in 1989, 690 of the 753 subjects eligible responding, a response rate of 88%.

The interview schedule covered information on customary physical health, mental functioning, psychological well-being, contact with health and social services together with socio-economic status and other demographic characteristics. In addition anthropometric measurements of hand-grip strength, shoulder flexibility, stature and body-weight were made on completion of each interview. Full descriptions of the design and methods of the NLSAA can be found elsewhere (Morgan et al, 1987; 1989).

9.2 The Melton Mowbray Aging Project (MMAP)

The Melton Mowbray Aging Project (MMAP) consists of two cross-sectional surveys (1981 and 1988) and an intermediate follow-up (1985) of survivors of all patients aged 75 years and over who were registered with the Latham House general practice. This practice of 13 doctors serves the town of Melton Mowbray, Leicestershire and the surrounding rural area and encompasses the majority of the administrative region of Melton District. Community and institutional residents were included in both cohorts and follow-ups. One thousand, two hundred and three subjects formed the initial cohort with 93% (1124) living in the community and 7% (79) interviewed in hospitals, nursing or residential homes. Six hundred and two people out of a possible 651 completed the first follow-up interview. The second cross-section in 1988 comprised 1579 subjects aged 75 years and over, 440 of these being survivors from the 1981 cohort.

All three survey instruments covered demographic information, physical and mental functioning and use of health and social services. Additionally, in the 1988 study, all those scoring 21 or under (out of a possible 30) on the Mini-Mental State examination (Folstein, 1975), 1 in 2 of those scoring 22 or 23 and 1 in 10 of the remainder had a full psychiatric interview, providing clinical evidence of dementia (including subtypes). Full details of the design and methods of the MMAP can be found elsewhere (Clarke et al, 1984, 1991; Jagger et al, 1989, 1991).

9.3 Comparison of survey instruments

The basis for this pilot study was the overlap of information on basic social, physical and mental functioning between the NLSAA and MMAP. Demographic data such as social class, household composition and marital status; mental functioning in the form of the Information/Orientation (IO) subtest of the CAPE assessment (Pattie and Gilleard, 1979) and use of health and social services were collected identically and coded equivalently in the NLSAA and MMAP.

Information on vision; hearing; urinary incontinence; mobility around the house; self-perceived health were collected similarly in the NLSAA and MMAP though not identically. Activities of daily living (ADLs) such as getting in and out of a bed or chair or to the toilet, feeding and dressing were collected mainly in the MMAP but some imputations can be made from the NLSAA for these data.

The variables collected solely by the NLSAA included measures of strength and joint flexibility, mental health status using the Symptoms of Anxiety and Depression scale (SAD) (Bedford et al, 1976), psychological well-being by the Life Satisfaction Index (LSI) (Neugarten et al, 1961) and a physical health assessment comprising a checklist of symptoms (Morgan et al, 1991). Those items included in the MMAP only were mainly ADL and IADL items to enable production of the Katz ADL scale (Katz and Akpom, 1976) and the critical interval need scale (Isaacs and Neville, 1976);

a physical disability scale devised from the 1981 data (Jagger et al, 1986); morale as measured by the 17-item Philadelphia Geriatric Center Morale Scale (Morris and Sherwood, 1975) subsequently amended by Wenger (1984) (1988 only); the clinical diagnoses of dementia and depression (1988 only); difficulty managing on income. Although IADLs were collected in NLSAA the question asked only who performed the task not whether each subject was able to perform. In the first wave of the MMAP, IADLs were assessed only of households, thus the critical interval need scale and IADL scale are shown only for the 1988 wave of the MMAP.

9.4 Comparison of NLSAA and MMAP baseline populations

The demographic characteristics of the baseline populations for those living in the community in the MMAP and those aged 75 years and over in the NLSAA were compared (Table 9.1). There were no significant differences between the NLSAA and the MMAP for the distributions of age (χ^2=2.88, df=3, p=0.41), sex (χ^2=0.27, df=1, p=0.60) or marital status (χ^2=4.87, df=2, p=0.09). The NLSAA appeared to have fewer subjects aged 75 years and over in the higher social classes (χ^2=14.24, df=3, p=0.003) and significantly more of the NLSAA sample of this age were living alone (χ^2=8.9, df=1, p=0.003). Although by 1988 in Melton Mowbray the proportion of those living alone in the community had risen slightly from 45% to 49%, the differences in social class and numbers living alone between the NLSAA and MMAP are more in line with the NLSAA sample being residents of inner city suburbs.

Table 9.1: Comparison of the baseline populations from NLSAA (subjects 75 years and over only) and MMAP (community dwelling residents only)

	NLSAA Percentage (N)	MMAP Percentage (N)
Age at interview		
75-79 yrs	51.9 (276)	55.4 (623)
80-84 yrs	33.7 (179)	30.0 (337)
85-89 yrs	10.0 (53)	10.7 (120)
≥ 90 yrs	4.5 (24)	3.9 (44)
Sex		
Males	34.0 (181)	32.7 (368)
Females	66.0 (351)	67.3 (756)
Marital status		
Single	6.6 (35)	6.3 (71)
Married	32.0 (170)	37.9 (426)
Widowed/separated/ divorced	60.3 (321)	55.8 (627)
Missing	1.1 (6)	0.0 (0)
Household composition		
Living alone	57.1 (304)	45.4 (510)
Not living alone	41.7 (222)	54.6 (514)
Missing	1.1 (6)	0.0 (0)
Social class		
I + II	16.0 (85)	22.2 (249)
III	56.6 (301)	47.6 (535)
IV + V	25.0 (133)	26.7 (301)
unclassifiable	2.4 (13)	13.5 (39)

9.5 Comparison of NLSAA and MMAP with national mortality and census data

The two studies were chosen for their comparability in design and outcome measurements with each other rather than their being representative of a national elderly population. However, it is of interest, where possible, to assess the degree to which demographic characteristics, morbidity and mortality might differ from national figures.

As reported in section 9.1, the sampling frame of general practices for the NLSAA was chosen to be representative of England and Wales in terms of age, sex, ethnicity and social class distributions. The distributions of age group within sex, marital status and the sex ratios within age groups for MMAP, NLSAA and England and Wales (OPCS, 1981) show broad similarities (Table 9.2). The MMAP and NLSAA however appear to have a smaller percentage of very elderly men than the national population and the NLSAA also has smaller proportions of women in this age group. This is likely to be due to the omission of institutionalised elderly in the NLSAA.

Comparisons of more recent data of the geographical areas from which the studies arose (Melton District and Nottingham) with national death rates for the period 1990-1992 with 1991 census populations suggest that after age and sex adjustment, mortality rates in Melton are similar to national rates whilst rates for Nottingham are slightly higher (J. Charlton, personal communication). Over this time period, the SMR for Melton District is 96 with 95% confidence interval (91, 102) whilst that for Nottingham is 103 (101, 105).

Table 9.2: Comparison of MMAP and NLSAA with England and Wales

	MMAP Percentage (N)	NLSAA Percentage (N)	England & Wales Percentage (N)
Males % (N)			
75-79 years	64.2 (244)	60.2 (109)	59.4 (566,200)
80-84 years	24.0 (91)	29.8 (54)	27.4 (261,000)
≥ 85 years	11.8 (45)	9.9 (18)	13.2 (125,500)
Females % (N)			
75-79 years	48.2 (397)	47.6 (167)	48.6 (958,800)
80-84 years	31.5 (259)	35.6 (125)	30.6 (603,800)
≥ 85 years	20.3 (167)	16.8 (59)	20.8 (410,700)
65-74 years % (N)			
Married	-	62.3 (315)	62.8 (2,917,800)
Single	-	5.3 (27)	9.1 (423,600)
Widowed/Divorced/ Separated	-	32.4 (164)	28.1 (1,304,700)
≥ 75 Years % (N)			
Married	37.9 (426)	32.2 (170)	33.9 (991,100)
Single	6.3 (71)	6.7 (35)	11.7 (342,400)
Widowed/Divorced/ Separated	55.8 (627)	61.0 (321)	54.4 (1,592,500)
Female:Male			
65-74 years	-	1.26	1.29
≥ 75 years	1.94	2.05	2.14

10 Health expectancies under differing definitions of health: cross-sectional estimates

Prevalence data for various health states from the NLSAA, MMAP and the 1988 Melton Mowbray cohort enables cross-sectional estimates of health expectancies at three time points, 1981, 1985 and 1988. The health expectancies were calculated by Sullivan's method (described in chapter 4) using England and Wales mortality rates for the relevant years, these being formed from deaths for three years centred on the relevant study year (e.g. 1984-6 for the NLSAA) and the estimated population at the study year (e.g. 1985 for the NLSAA).

People living in institutions were excluded from all measures in the NLSAA and certain ones in the MMAP. As noted in chapter 5, calculations of health expectations using prevalence for the non-institutionalised only can be misleading since the rate of institutionalisation rises sharply with increasing age. The baseline cohort of the MMAP included people in institutions, hence for health expectancies calculated from this data source, persons in institutions were included in the 'poor health' or 'disabled' state. Prevalence was thus calculated as proportions of the age group and sex who were in a particular state of disability or institutionalised. No such data were available for the NLSAA and therefore the expected numbers in institutions given the sample size were required for each age group and sex. These were calculated as the average rate of institutionalisation from two censuses of all people aged 65 years and over in residential care throughout the county of Leicestershire in 1979 and 1990 (Campbell Stern et al, 1993). These expected numbers in institutions were included in the 'poor health' state as with the MMAP.

Tables 10.1-10.17 show the changes in life expectancy in various states of health over time with the corresponding age and sex specific prevalence in Appendix B Tables B.1 - B.12. For each time point the percentage of life (at a particular age) free of the state of ill-health is calculated. Total life expectancy at all ages has increased very slightly over the period 1981 to 1988. At age 75 years women can expect to live around 2.5 years more than men although differences in health expectancies are not as marked. For the majority of health states considered, the percentage of life spent free of ill-health drops markedly with age. In general women spend a lower percentage of their remaining life healthy than men, a finding consistent with almost every country where such calculations have been made (Bone, 1992). The expectation of life without disability for the UK in 1981 has been estimated as 7.7 years for men and 8.1 years for women aged 65, 4.0 years for men and 3.7 years for women aged 75 using the limiting long-standing illness question from the General Household Survey (Bebbington, 1988).

Standard errors on the expected life without disability or impairment were calculated as described by Bebbington (1988). To retain clarity, these have not been included in each table but guidelines are given here to determine whether differences between time points at given ages reach statistical significance. For men at all three time points, the standard errors on the expectation of life without disability were of magnitude 0.1 years at age 75 years to around 0.5 years at age 90. DFLE for women had standard errors in the region of 0.15 at age 75 years to 0.4 at 90 years. Differences in DFLE estimates greater than 0.3 years for men at 75 years of age would reach significance at the 5% level as would differences in DFLE estimates at age 90 greater than 1.4 years. The corresponding figures for women are 0.4 years at age 75 and 1.1 years at age 90.

10.1 Mental impairment

The prevalence of mental impairment varies dramatically depending on the instrument or indeed the cutpoint used for definition (Tables B.1 - B.2). After adjusting for age and sex differences, the prevalence of mental impairment from both years of the MMAP were significantly lower than those from the NLSAA (χ^2=24.90, df=2, p<0.001) with the differences varying significantly with age (χ^2=10.84, df=4, p=0.03). Despite this, the majority of remaining life for men and women appears to be spent free of mental impairment (Tables 10.1 - 10.3). Life expectancies with impairment are found to be around 6-8 months for men and between 1 and 1.5 years for women, using the Information/Orientation subtest of the CAPE assessment. Estimates based on the Mini-Mental State Examination result in higher prevalence and therefore longer life with impairment. The differences between these screening tests have been examined (Clarke et al, 1991; Jagger et al, 1992a, 1992b), particularly the tendency for elderly people free of mental impairment but with sensory or physical impairments to achieve lower scores on the Mini-Mental State Examination. Life expectancies with dementia from France are relatively constant across age, being around 0.6 years for men and 0.9 years for women (Ritchie et al, 1992). The estimates from MMAP appear in line with these, taking into account the differences in study design and diagnostic instrument.

10.2 Impairments of vision and hearing

Women appear to spend almost twice the number of remaining years of life with vision impairments than men (Table 10.4). These sex differences are largely due to the increased survival in women since prevalences are not consistently higher for women (Table B.3). Age and sex specific prevalence between NLSAA and 1981 MMAP were

Table 10.1: Life expectancies with minimal, mild, moderate and severe clinically diagnosed dementia 1988 (MMAP)

Age (yrs)	Life expectancy (yrs)					
	Total (a)	Dementia Free (b)	With minimal severity	With mild severity	With dementia mod/severe	(b)/(a) (%)
Males						
75	8.43	6.22	1.06	0.84	0.30	73.8
80	6.45	4.23	0.85	1.01	0.35	65.6
85	5.00	2.64	1.14	0.65	0.57	52.7
90	4.13	1.03	1.03	1.03	1.03	25.0
Females						
75	10.94	6.41	2.52	1.19	0.83	58.6
80	8.15	3.63	2.35	1.29	0.89	44.5
85	5.94	1.60	2.06	1.27	1.01	26.9
90	4.34	1.32	0.66	1.13	1.23	30.4

Table 10.2: Life expectancies with mental impairment defined as Mini-Mental State Examination score 24 or less (1988 MMAP)

Age (yrs)	Life expectancy (yrs)			
	Total (a)	Free of impairment (b)	With mental impairment	(b)/(a) (%)
Males				
75	8.43	5.97	2.46	70.8
80	6.45	3.96	2.43	60.3
85	5.00	2.65	2.35	52.9
90	4.13	2.29	1.83	55.6
Females				
75	10.94	5.99	4.95	54.7
80	8.15	3.49	4.66	42.8
85	5.94	1.62	4.32	27.3
90	4.34	0.83	3.52	19.0

similar though the rates by 1988 MMAP had fallen significantly (χ^2=266.8, df=2, p<0.0001). A possible reason for this decrease in visual impairment was an increased focus on research in community-living elderly by the Department of Ophthalmology at the University of Leicester with the subsequent introduction of an eye clinic at the Latham House practice in 1991. Figures from the US suggest that visual impairment ranks highly as a cause of limitation in activity in those aged 65 years and over (Verbrugge, 1989). Cataracts, glaucoma, diabetic retinopathy and senile macular degeneration account for 86% of poor vision in those aged over 75 years (Leibowitz et al, 1980).

Rates of hearing impairment showed a similar pattern to those for vision with the two earlier studies being closer than the later one (χ^2=215.0, df=2, p<0.0001). Hearing impairment ranks as one of the leading chronic conditions in elderly people both in the US (Verbrugge, 1989) and the Netherlands (van den Berg Jeths et al, 1994). Prevalence rates in the US appear to be slightly lower for women than men (Verbrugge, 1989) and this is supported here (Table B.4). The number of years of remaining life spent free of hearing impairment at

age 75 is significantly greater for women than men (Table 10.5) though when this is expressed as a proportion of remaining life men and women show less difference.

10.3 Urinary incontinence

The age and sex specific prevalence of urinary incontinence from the three studies are shown in Table B.5, the rates from the NLSAA being significantly greater than those from MMAP (χ^2=59.71, df=2, p<0.001). Table 10.6 suggests that life expectancy with urinary incontinence has increased somewhat for women from 1981 to 1988 due to the accompanying rise in prevalence. This may be a consequence of the subjective nature of the measure of urinary incontinence, being gained verbally from the subject. Women may have been less inclined to admit to incontinence in the earlier study, resulting in lower prevalence and therefore lower life expectancies with incontinence. Urinary incontinence can cause considerable limitations in activity and social functioning of elderly people and is a major reason for institutionalisation.

10.4 Physical disabilities and impairments of mobility

Four measures of physical disability were investigated, difficulty getting out of doors, difficulties with mobility requiring the help of another person, the Physical Disability Scale (Jagger et al, 1986) and the Katz ADL scale (Katz and Akpom, 1976) (Tables 10.7 - 10.10). The Physical Disability Scale incorporates the five ADLs of transfer from bed and chair, dressing, mobility around the home and going to the toilet with the use of aids scored as a separate category. The Katz ADL scale includes the ADLs feeding, bathing, dressing, transfer from bed or chair and classifies subjects as unable to perform only if they require the help of a person.

Physical disability as measured by difficulty with mobility appeared to have similar levels over time in the MMAP (Table B.6) though both were consistently lower than rates found by the NLSAA (χ^2=39.93, df=2, p<0.001). Table B.7 shows that significantly lower rates of disability were observed in 1988 compared to 1981 with both moderate and severe disability using the Physical Disability Scale (χ^2=9.23,

Table 10.3: Life expectancies with mental impairment (mental impairment defined as IO score of 8 or under) for 1981 (MMAP), 1985 (NLSAA) and 1988 (MMAP)

Age (yrs)	1981 (MMAP)				1985 (NLSAA)				1988 (MMAP)			
	TLE[1] (yrs)	DFLE[2] (yrs)	DLE[3] (yrs)	DFLE/ TLE (%)	TLE[1] (yrs)	DFLE[2] (yrs)	DLE[3] (yrs)	DFLE/ TLE (%)	TLE[1] (yrs)	DFLE[2] (yrs)	DLE[3] (yrs)	DFLE/ TLE (%)
Males												
65					13.42	12.30	1.12	91.7				
70					10.48	9.37	1.12	89.4				
75	7.72	7.14	0.58	92.5	7.80	6.85	1.15	85.7	8.43	7.78	0.65	92.3
80	5.80	5.22	0.58	90.0	6.02	5.01	1.01	83.3	6.45	5.67	0.78	87.9
85	4.36	3.67	0.69	84.2	4.52	3.48	1.05	76.9	5.00	4.12	0.88	82.4
90	3.55	2.58	0.97	72.7	3.62	2.78	0.84	76.9	4.13	2.75	1.38	66.7
Females												
65					17.37	15.41	1.96	88.8				
70					13.80	11.84	1.96	85.8				
75	10.21	8.99	1.21	88.1	10.57	8.54	2.03	80.8	10.94	9.47	1.47	86.6
80	7.50	6.23	1.27	83.0	7.80	5.82	1.98	74.6	8.15	6.51	1.64	79.9
85	5.39	3.80	1.59	70.4	5.61	3.53	2.08	62.9	5.94	4.20	1.73	70.8
90	4.01	2.50	1.51	62.3	4.09	2.57	1.52	62.9	4.34	2.65	1.70	60.9

[1] Total life expectancy
[2] Disability (mental impairment)-free life expectancy
[3] Life expectancy with disability (mental impairment)

Table 10.4: Life expectancies with visual impairment (visual impairment defined as difficulty with vision) or institutionalised for 1981 (MMAP), 1985 (NLSAA) and 1988 (MMAP)

Age (yrs)	1981 (MMAP)				1985 (NLSAA)				1988 (MMAP)			
	TLE[1] (yrs)	DFLE[2] (yrs)	DLE[3] (yrs)	DFLE/ TLE (%)	TLE[1] (yrs)	DFLE[2] (yrs)	DLE[3] (yrs)	DFLE/ TLE (%)	TLE[1] (yrs)	DFLE[2] (yrs)	DLE[3] (yrs)	DFLE/ TLE (%)
Males												
65					13.42	10.62	2.80	79.2				
70					10.48	8.02	2.47	76.5				
75	7.72	5.52	2.20	71.5	8.00	5.50	2.49	68.8	8.43	7.28	1.15	86.4
80	5.80	3.94	1.86	68.0	6.02	3.16	2.86	52.4	6.45	5.35	1.10	84.0
85	4.36	2.53	1.83	57.9	4.52	1.74	2.79	38.5	5.00	4.02	0.98	80.4
90	3.55	2.13	1.42	60.0	3.62	1.39	2.23	38.5	4.13	3.67	0.46	88.9
Females												
65					17.37	12.27	5.10	70.6				
70					13.80	8.89	4.91	64.5				
75	10.21	5.61	4.60	54.9	10.57	5.88	4.69	55.6	10.94	9.15	1.79	83.7
80	7.50	3.45	4.05	46.0	7.81	3.55	4.26	45.5	8.15	6.29	1.86	77.1
85	5.39	1.61	3.78	29.9	5.61	2.22	3.83	39.7	5.94	4.03	1.90	67.9
90	4.01	0.82	3.19	20.3	4.09	1.62	2.47	39.7	4.34	2.31	2.04	53.1

[1] Total life expectancy
[2] Disability (visual impairment or institutionalised)-free life expectancy
[3] Life expectancy with disability (visual impairment or institutionalised)

Table 10.5: Life expectancies with hearing impairment (hearing impairment defined as difficulty with hearing) or institutionalised for 1981 (MMAP), 1985 (NLSAA) and 1988 (MMAP)

Age (yrs)	1981 (MMAP)				1985 (NLSAA)				1988 (MMAP)			
	TLE[1] (yrs)	DFLE[2] (yrs)	DLE[3] (yrs)	DFLE/ TLE (%)	TLE[1] (yrs)	DFLE[2] (yrs)	DLE[3] (yrs)	DFLE/ TLE (%)	TLE[1] (yrs)	DFLE[2] (yrs)	DLE[3] (yrs)	DFLE/ TLE (%)
Males												
65					13.42	8.25	5.17	61.5				
70					10.48	6.16	4.32	58.8				
75	7.72	3.60	4.12	46.6	8.00	3.81	4.19	47.6	8.43	5.89	2.54	69.9
80	5.80	2.07	3.73	35.7	6.02	2.24	3.78	37.2	6.45	3.76	2.69	58.3
85	4.36	1.43	2.93	32.8	4.52	1.09	3.44	24.0	5.00	2.27	2.73	45.3
90	3.55	1.29	2.26	36.4	3.62	0.87	2.75	24.0	4.13	1.83	2.29	44.4
Females												
65					17.37	11.60	5.77	66.8				
70					13.80	8.25	5.55	59.8				
75	10.21	5.48	4.73	53.7	10.57	5.42	5.15	51.3	10.94	8.08	2.86	73.8
80	7.50	3.25	4.26	43.4	7.81	3.23	4.58	41.3	8.15	5.25	2.90	64.4
85	5.39	1.46	3.93	27.1	5.61	1.59	4.02	28.3	5.94	2.93	3.01	49.3
90	4.01	0.59	3.42	14.8	4.09	1.16	2.93	28.3	4.34	1.49	2.85	34.3

[1] Total life expectancy
[2] Disability (hearing impairment or institutionalised)-free life expectancy
[3] Life expectancy with disability (hearing impairment or institutionalised)

Table 10.6: Life expectancies with urinary incontinence for 1981 (MMAP), 1985 (NLSAA) and 1988 (MMAP)

Age (yrs)	1981 (MMAP)				1985 (NLSAA)				1988 (MMAP)			
	TLE[1] (yrs)	DFLE[2] (yrs)	DLE[3] (yrs)	DFLE/ TLE (%)	TLE[1] (yrs)	DFLE[2] (yrs)	DLE[3] (yrs)	DFLE/ TLE (%)	TLE[1] (yrs)	DFLE[2] (yrs)	DLE[3] (yrs)	DFLE/ TLE (%)
Males												
65					13.42	11.46	1.96	85.4				
70					10.48	8.64	1.85	82.4				
75	7.72	6.69	1.03	86.6	8.00	6.18	1.82	77.3	8.43	7.63	0.80	90.5
80	5.80	4.85	0.95	83.6	6.02	4.49	1.53	74.7	6.45	5.77	0.68	89.4
85	4.36	3.49	0.87	80.1	4.52	3.22	1.30	71.3	5.00	4.31	0.69	86.3
90	3.55	2.58	0.97	72.7	3.62	2.58	1.04	71.3	4.13	3.76	0.46	88.9
Females												
65					17.37	13.24	4.13	76.2				
70					13.80	10.19	3.61	73.8				
75	10.21	8.92	1.29	87.4	10.57	7.57	3.00	71.6	10.94	9.15	1.79	83.6
80	7.50	6.34	1.16	84.5	7.81	5.15	2.66	66.0	8.15	6.51	1.64	79.9
85	5.39	4.35	1.05	80.6	5.61	3.56	2.05	63.4	5.94	4.44	1.49	74.8
90	4.01	3.42	0.59	85.2	4.09	2.59	1.50	63.4	4.34	2.90	1.45	66.7

[1] Total life expectancy
[2] Disability (urinary incontinence)-free life expectancy
[3] Life expectancy with disability (urinary incontinence)

Table 10.7: Life expectancies with difficulty getting outdoors or institutionalised for 1981 (MMAP) and 1988 (MMAP)

Age (yrs)	1981 (MMAP)				1988 (MMAP)			
	TLE[1] (yrs)	DFLE[2] (yrs)	DLE[3] (yrs)	DFLE/ TLE (%)	TLE[1] (yrs)	DFLE[2] (yrs)	DLE[3] (yrs)	DFLE/ TLE (%)
Males								
75	7.72	4.83	2.89	62.5	8.43	5.45	2.98	64.6
80	5.80	3.05	2.75	52.5	6.45	3.50	2.95	54.3
85	4.36	1.62	2.74	37.3	5.00	2.07	2.93	41.5
90	3.55	1.07	2.49	30.0	4.13	1.83	2.29	44.4
Females								
75	10.21	4.75	5.46	46.5	10.94	5.40	5.54	49.3
80	7.50	2.45	5.05	32.7	8.15	2.98	5.17	36.5
85	5.39	0.90	4.49	16.7	5.94	1.28	4.66	21.5
90	4.01	0.61	3.40	15.3	4.34	0.48	3.87	10.9

[1] Total life expectancy
[2] Disability-free life expectancy
[3] Life expectancy with disability

Table 10.8: Life expectancies with mobility impairment for 1981 (MMAP), 1985 (NLSAA) and 1988 (MMAP)

Age (yrs)	1981 (MMAP)				1985 (NLSAA)				1988 (MMAP)			
	TLE[1] (yrs)	DFLE[2] (yrs)	DLE[3] (yrs)	DFLE/ TLE (%)	TLE[1] (yrs)	DFLE[2] (yrs)	DLE[3] (yrs)	DFLE/ TLE (%)	TLE[1] (yrs)	DFLE[2] (yrs)	DLE[3] (yrs)	DFLE/ TLE (%)
Males												
65					13.42	12.80	0.61	95.4				
70					10.48	9.81	0.67	93.6				
75	7.72	7.50	0.22	97.2	8.00	7.30	0.70	91.3	8.43	8.25	0.18	97.8
80	5.80	5.59	0.21	96.3	6.02	5.36	0.66	89.1	6.45	6.24	0.21	96.7
85	4.36	4.25	0.11	97.5	4.52	3.91	0.61	86.5	5.00	4.72	0.28	94.4
90	3.55	3.23	0.32	90.9	3.62	3.13	0.49	86.5	4.13	3.23	0.00	100.0
Females												
65					17.37	15.96	1.40	91.9				
70					13.80	12.45	1.35	90.2				
75	10.21	9.66	0.55	94.6	10.57	9.30	1.27	88.0	10.94	10.38	0.56	94.8
80	7.50	6.96	0.54	92.9	7.81	6.54	1.27	83.8	8.15	7.56	0.59	92.7
85	5.39	4.79	0.60	88.9	5.61	4.45	1.16	79.4	5.94	5.27	0.67	88.8
90	4.01	3.25	0.66	83.6	4.09	3.30	0.79	80.7	4.34	3.65	0.69	84.1

[1] Total life expectancy
[2] Disability-free life expectancy
[3] Life expectancy with disability

Table 10.9: Life expectancies with moderate or severe physical disability (defined by Physical Disability scale) for 1981 (MMAP) and 1988 (MMAP)

Age (yrs)	1981 (MMAP)				1988 (MMAP)			
	TLE[1] (yrs)	DFLE[2] (yrs)	DLE[3] (yrs)	DFLE/ TLE (%)	TLE[1] (yrs)	DFLE[2] (yrs)	DLE[3] (yrs)	DFLE/ TLE (%)
Males								
75	7.72	6.14	1.58	79.6	8.43	6.80	1.63	80.7
80	5.80	4.28	1.52	73.7	6.45	4.69	1.76	72.7
85	4.36	2.73	1.63	62.6	5.00	3.24	1.76	64.7
90	3.55	1.94	1.61	54.5	4.13	3.21	0.92	77.8
Females								
75	10.21	7.45	2.76	72.9	10.94	8.02	2.92	73.3
80	7.50	4.80	2.70	64.0	8.15	5.15	3.00	63.2
85	5.39	2.78	2.62	51.5	5.94	3.00	2.93	50.6
90	4.01	1.58	2.43	39.3	4.34	1.86	2.48	42.9

[1] Total life expectancy
[2] Disability-free life expectancy
[3] Life expectancy with disability

Table 10.10: Life expectancies dependent in 1 or more ADLs (defined by Katz ADL scale) for 1981 (MMAP) and 1988 (MMAP)

Age (yrs)	1981 (MMAP)				1988 (MMAP)			
	TLE[1] (yrs)	DFLE[2] (yrs)	DLE[3] (yrs)	DFLE/ TLE (%)	TLE[1] (yrs)	DFLE[2] (yrs)	DLE[3] (yrs)	DFLE/ TLE (%)
Males								
75	7.72	6.41	1.31	83.0	8.43	6.86	1.57	81.4
80	5.80	4.60	1.20	79.3	6.45	4.78	1.67	74.1
85	4.36	3.22	1.14	73.9	5.00	3.49	1.51	69.7
90	3.55	2.58	0.96	72.7	4.13	2.75	1.38	66.7
Females								
75	10.21	7.16	3.05	70.1	10.94	7.71	3.23	70.5
80	7.50	4.53	2.97	60.4	8.15	4.86	3.29	59.7
85	5.39	2.54	2.85	47.2	5.94	2.58	3.35	43.5
90	4.01	0.99	3.02	24.6	4.34	1.72	2.62	39.7

[1] Total life expectancy
[2] Disability-free life expectancy
[3] Life expectancy with disability

df=1, p=0.002) and difficulty getting out of doors (χ^2=4.84, df=1, p=0.028) whilst the Katz ADL scale showed no significant change over time (χ^2=0.83, df=1, p=0.36).

The proportion of life spent free of disability is greatest at all ages when disability is requiring the help of another to be mobile around the home. In all cases women spend a greater proportion of their remaining years with disability, the greatest sex differences appearing with difficulty getting out of doors. Similar figures to those in Table 10.10 were found by Rogers et al (1990) who estimated the active life expectancy at 80 years of age for both sexes combined to be 4.85 years, this being 63% of total life expectancy at 80 years. These figures are calculated from the 1986 US Longitudinal Study of Aging and are based on dependence in one or more of seven ADLs or being institutionalised. The expectation of life without bed disability or long-term institutionalisation has been estimated as 14.2 years for men

and 18.4 years for women at 65 in the US (Crimmins et al, 1989). Figures for England and Wales in 1987 based on limiting long-standing illness were 13.7 years for men and 17.6 for women. The expectation of life free of mobility impairment at 65 years is 12.8 for men and 16.0 for women (Table 10.8).

Both prevalence rates (Table B.8) and life expectancies (Table 10.11) with dependence in IADLs are greater than those with dependence in ADLs, reflecting that Instrumental ADLs are lost sooner than personal care abilities. Combining IADLs and ADLs into the critical interval need scale demonstrates the problems that the form of the IADL questions may have for men. Tables 10.12 and B.8 show that men have much higher age specific rates of disability than women and consequently spend a much higher proportion of remaining life with short or critical interval need or institutionalised. Short interval need is defined as requiring

Table 10.11: Life expectancies with reduced IADL (reduced IADL defined as unable to perform 2 or more IADLs) or institutionalised 1988 (MMAP)

Age (yrs)	Life expectancy (years)			
	TLE[1]	DFLE[2]	DLE[3]	DFLE/TLE (%)
Males				
75	8.43	5.93	2.50	70.3
80	6.45	4.45	2.00	69.0
85	5.00	3.40	1.60	68.1
90	4.13	2.75	1.38	66.7
Females				
75	10.94	5.53	5.41	50.5
80	8.15	3.56	4.59	43.7
85	5.94	2.64	3.30	44.4
90	4.34	2.21	2.13	50.9

[1]Total life expectancy
[2]Disability-free life expectancy
[3]Life expectancy with disability

Table 10.12: Life expectancies short or critical interval need or institutionalised 1988 (MMAP)

Age (yrs)	Life expectancy (yrs)			
	TLE[1]	DFLE[2]	DLE[3]	DFLE/TLE (%)
Males				
75	8.43	2.03	6.40	24.1
80	6.45	1.60	4.85	24.8
85	5.00	1.31	3.93	25.1
90	4.13	0.92	3.21	22.2
Females				
75	10.94	6.27	4.67	57.4
80	8.15	3.74	4.41	45.9
85	5.94	1.82	4.12	30.6
90	4.34	1.03	3.55	22.5

[1]Total life expectancy
[2]Disability-free life expectancy
[3]Life expectancy with disability

help to bath or dress or being unable to cook whilst those with critical interval need cannot rise from bed or chair or go to the toilet, are incontinent of faeces, severely cognitively impaired or incontinent of urine with added difficulty dressing. These results are likely to be confounded by the societal norms that men of this age do not usually undertake cooking and they highlight the need for careful formation of questions covering IADLs (and for some cultures ADLs) if they are to reflect the elderly person's ability to perform the task.

The decreased prevalence of disability over time as found by the MMAP result in the expected increase both in DFLE and in the proportion of total life expectancy spent free of disability (Table 10.9). However estimates also demonstrate the strong effect that changes in mortality have on DFLE calculated by this method. Despite decreases in disability, the decreases in mortality produce an increase in the number of years spent in all states, including being disabled.

10.5 Self perceived health

Poor self perceived health has been found to be a strong predictor of subsequent mortality and hospitalisation (Mossey and Shapiro, 1982; Weinberger et al, 1986; Jagger et al, 1988) even after adjustment for physical disability and other factors associated with reduced mortality. Proportions of life in good health for men appear to be maintained with increasing age whilst women again show the usual decline in the proportion of life spent in good health with age (Table 10.13). Comparable figures from the Netherlands show Healthy Life Percentage (proportion of life spent in good health) in 1985 to be 60% for men aged 65 years and 54% for women whilst in 1989 the figures were 58% for men and 47% for women. Differences in age and sex specific rates of poor and fair perceived health and institutionalisation (Table B.9) were found both between studies and within studies over time (χ^2=11.67, df=2, p=0.003) resulting in the appearance of decreasing Healthy Life Percentage over time. However the longer series from the Netherlands, from 1981 to 1990, suggest that the long-term trend for Healthy Life Percentage is a slight increase (Perenboom et al, 1992), although a different combination of categories results in an overall deterioration (Boshuizen, 1993).

10.6 Depression

Table 10.14 shows the estimates of life expectancy with and without depression. For the MMAP, depression was clinically diagnosed using the CAMDEX assessment categories of none versus mild, moderate or severe (Roth et al, 1988) whilst the NLSAA used the SAD scale (Bedford et al, 1976) with a score of 6 or over on the whole scale and a score of 4 or more on the depression subscale indicating significant depression. Depression has been found to be a common condition in old age though definitions vary. With the greater severity and clinical diagnosis considered here, prevalence, particularly in older men, were small (Table B.10) and thus estimates will have large confidence intervals. However, almost 90% of remaining life at all ages is spent free of depression. Using the Philadelphia Geriatric Morale Scale as modified by Wenger (1984) the sex differences are more marked with women again spending a larger proportion of their remaining life with low morale (Table 10.15 and B.10).

10.7 Global health

The emphasis on successful aging has drawn attention to those elderly people who have no disabilities or impairments common to their age group. To investigate this phenomenon in the two study populations, a global health measure was constructed which brought together the separate health measurements described earlier. A person was defined as healthy if they had no help with mobility, no visual or hearing impairments, an IO score of 11 or 12, perceived themselves to be in good health, were not incontinent and were not resident in an institution. Table B.11 gives the prevalence of global ill-health and Table 10.16 below the life expectancies in a state of good global health. Although the prevalence of any one of the conditions is high, in 1981 there were around 10% of those aged 85 years and over without any of the disabilities or impairments. By 1988 this figure had risen to almost 20%. Life expectancies free of any of the conditions formed a small proportion of total life expectancy for both men and women, but from the 1988 MMAP data, both men and women could expect to spend almost a further year free of these conditions at age 85.

Table 10.13: Life expectancies with poor or fair perceived health or institutionalised for 1981 (MMAP), 1985 (NLSAA) and 1988 (MMAP)

Age (yrs)	1981 (MMAP)				1985 (NLSAA)				1988 (MMAP)			
	TLE[1] (yrs)	HLE[2] (yrs)	LEWH[3] (yrs)	HLE/TLE (%)	TLE[1] (yrs)	HLE[2] (yrs)	LEWH[3] (yrs)	HLE/TLE (%)	TLE[1] (yrs)	HLE[2] (yrs)	LEWH[3] (yrs)	HLE/TLE (%)
Males												
65					13.42	8.41	5.01	62.7				
70					10.48	6.73	3.75	64.2				
75	7.72	4.68	3.04	60.7	8.00	5.13	2.86	64.2	8.43	4.78	3.65	56.7
80	5.80	3.45	2.35	59.5	6.02	3.99	2.02	66.4	6.45	3.67	2.70	57.1
85	4.36	2.77	1.59	63.5	4.52	3.26	1.26	72.1	5.00	3.13	1.87	62.6
90	3.55	2.58	0.97	72.7	3.62	2.61	1.01	72.1	4.13	3.21	0.92	77.8
Females												
65					17.37	8.33	9.03	48.0				
70					13.80	6.52	7.28	47.2				
75	10.21	5.43	4.78	53.2	10.57	5.13	5.44	48.5	10.94	5.02	5.92	45.9
80	7.50	3.77	3.72	50.3	7.81	3.93	3.87	50.4	8.15	3.63	4.52	44.5
85	5.39	2.41	2.98	46.4	5.61	2.74	2.87	48.8	5.94	2.40	3.53	40.5
90	4.01	1.67	2.34	41.7	4.09	2.00	2.09	48.8	4.34	1.56	2.78	35.9

[1] Total life expectancy
[2] Healthy life expectancy
[3] Life expectancy without good health or institutionalised

Table 10.14: Life expectancies with depression for 1985 (NLSAA) and 1988 (MMAP)

Age (yrs)	SAD scale significant depression for 1985 (NLSAA)				Mild, moderate or severe clinically diagnosed depression 1981 (MMAP)			
	TLE[1] (yrs)	DFLE[2] (yrs)	DLE[3] (yrs)	DFLE/TLE (%)	TLE[1] (yrs)	DFLE[2] (yrs)	DLE[3]	DFLE/TLE (%)
Males								
65	13.42	12.22	1.19	91.1				
70	10.48	9.51	0.97	90.7				
75	7.99	7.10	0.89	88.8	8.43	7.70	0.73	91.3
80	6.02	5.21	0.81	86.6	6.45	6.07	0.38	94.1
85	4.52	3.91	0.61	86.5	5.00	4.43	0.57	88.5
90	3.62	3.13	0.49	86.5	4.13	4.13	0.00	100.0
Females								
65	17.37	14.48	2.88	83.4				
70	13.80	11.43	2.36	82.9				
75	10.57	8.56	2.02	80.9	10.94	9.22	1.72	84.3
80	7.80	6.03	1.77	77.3	8.15	6.87	1.28	84.3
85	5.61	4.19	1.42	74.7	5.94	5.25	0.69	88.4
90	4.09	3.30	0.79	80.7	4.34	4.05	0.29	93.3

[1] Total life expectancy
[2] Depression free life expectancy
[3] Life expectancy with depression

Table 10.15:   Life expectancies with low morale or institutionalised for 1988 (MMAP)

Age (yrs)	1988 (MMAP)			
	TLE[1]	DFLE[2]	DLE[3]	DFLE/TLE (%)
Males				
75	8.43	7.13	1.30	84.6
80	6.45	5.16	1.29	80.1
85	5.00	3.97	1.03	79.5
90	4.13	2.32	1.38	66.7
Females				
75	10.94	7.89	3.05	72.1
80	8.15	5.58	2.57	68.5
85	5.94	3.58	2.36	60.2
90	4.34	2.31	2.03	53.2

[1] Total life expectancy
[2] Depression (low morale) free life expectancy
[3] Life expectancy with depression (low morale)

Table 10.16:   Life expectancies with global ill-health for 1981 (MMAP), 1985 (NLSAA) and 1988 (MMAP)

Age (yrs)	1981 (MMAP)				1985 (NLSAA)				1988 (MMAP)			
	TLE[1] (yrs)	DFLE[2] (yrs)	DLE[3] (yrs)	DFLE/ TLE (%)	TLE[1] (yrs)	DFLE[2] (yrs)	DLE[3] (yrs)	DFLE/ TLE (%)	TLE[1] (yrs)	DFLE[2] (yrs)	DLE[3] (yrs)	DFLE/ TLE (%)
Males												
65					13.42	3.94	9.48	29.4				
70					10.48	2.75	7.73	26.3				
75	7.72	1.68	6.04	21.7	8.00	1.38	6.62	17.2	8.43	2.95	5.48	34.9
80	5.80	0.96	4.84	16.5	6.02	0.45	5.56	7.6	6.45	1.84	4.61	28.5
85	4.36	0.38	3.98	8.7	4.52	0.00	4.52	0.0	5.00	0.85	4.15	17.1
90	3.55	0.32	3.23	9.1	3.62	0.00	3.90	0.0	4.13	0.46	3.67	11.1
Females												
65					17.37	3.70	13.67	21.3				
70					13.80	2.38	11.42	17.3				
75	10.21	2.00	8.20	19.6	10.57	1.30	9.28	12.3	10.94	3.29	7.65	30.1
80	7.50	0.96	6.54	12.8	7.81	0.57	7.23	7.3	8.15	1.99	6.16	24.4
85	5.39	0.36	5.03	6.8	5.61	0.22	5.39	3.9	5.94	0.96	4.97	16.2
90	4.01	0.13	3.88	3.3	4.09	0.00	4.09	0.0	4.34	0.55	3.79	12.7

[1] Total life expectancy
[2] Life expectancy free of mental and physical disability and in good health
[3] Life expectancy with mental and physical disability and less than good health

Table 10.17: Life expectancies with Health Index score of 1 or greater for 1985 (NLSAA)

Age (yrs)	1985 (NLSAA)			
	TLE[1]	DFLE[2]	DLE[3]	DFLE/TLE (%)
Males				
65	13.42	0.97	12.44	7.3
70	10.48	0.61	9.87	5.8
75	8.00	0.37	7.63	4.6
80	6.02	0.33	5.69	5.4
85	4.52	0.25	4.27	5.6
90	3.62	0.00	3.62	0.0
Females				
65	17.37	0.54	16.82	3.1
70	13.80	0.32	13.48	2.3
75	10.57	0.18	10.39	1.7
80	7.81	0.10	7.71	1.2
85	5.61	0.10	5.51	1.8
90	4.09	0.21	3.88	5.0

[1] Total life expectancy

[2] Disability and symptom free life expectancy

[3] Life expectancy with disability and/or symptoms

Another global measure of health was collected in the NLSAA (Morgan et al, 1991), this being a 14-item checklist of symptoms and disabilities covering presence or absence of problems with heart, stomach, eyesight, locomotion or feet; giddiness, headaches, incontinence, arthritis, insomnia and falls; long-term disabilities; use of drugs and medical services. For the purposes of analysis here, the scale was dichotomised into no recorded problems/any of the above and institutionalised included into the ill-health state by weighting appropriately. Not surprisingly the prevalence of ill-health using this scale was higher than that using the global scale as more conditions were included (Table B.12) and the corresponding life expectancies with health were smaller (Table 10.17)

11   Health expectancies under differing definitions of health: longitudinal estimates

The multistate life table model (Ledent, 1980; Rogers et al, 1990), outlined in chapter 4, has been used to calculate health expectancies from the two longitudinal studies, MMAP and NLSAA, combined. Rather than beginning with a single cohort, as does Sullivan's method, the multistate method has two (or more) subpopulations corresponding to two initial states of, say, healthy and unhealthy. More than two initial states may reflect a grading of ill-health or severity. The observed transition rates to the other state and to death are modelled to assess the effect of age and sex and the expected transition rates, under the final model, are used to calculate the probabilities of transitions between the states. The transition proportions from healthy to unhealthy and unhealthy to healthy are applied to the two subpopulations along with the transitions to death from either state. Hence, not only are recoveries from unhealthy to healthy allowed for, but the death rates of the two subpopulations can also differ.

The relatively small sizes of both the MMAP and NLSAA precluded the consideration of more than two health states

for each measure. For the purpose of this example the two states will be referred to as 'healthy' and 'unhealthy'. For each sex and five year age group (65-69, 70-74, 75-79, 80-84, 85-89, 90+ years), six transition rates between first survey and follow-up were calculated, as shown in Figure 11.1. The smoothed transition rates with respect to age were calculated by fitting piecewise exponential models with age group and sex as covariates. The fitted rates from state i (i=0,1) to state j (j=0,1,2) for age group x and sex s (s=1,2), $_{ij}\mu_{sx}$ satisfy

$$\ln {}_{ij}\mu_{sx} = {}_{ij}\alpha + {}_{ij}\beta_x + {}_{ij}\gamma_s$$

where α denotes the intercept term, β the coefficient for the age effect and γ the coefficient for the sex effect from the model and the i,j refer to the states in Figure 11.1. The usual model fitting techniques were employed to ascertain the best fitting model (i.e. to assess whether the rates differed by sex and/or age) and the results for each measure are given in Table 11.1.

Figure 11.1:   Possible transitions between states at first survey and follow-up

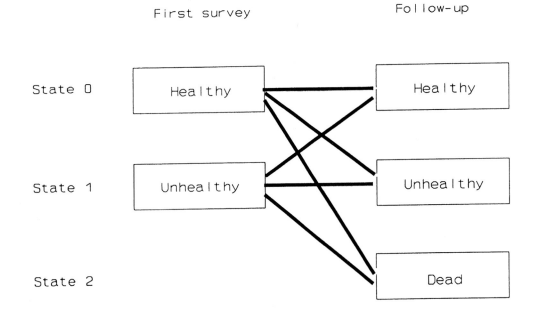

Table 11.1:   Significant associations of age and sex on transition rates

Health measure		Healthy to unhealthy	Healthy to death	Unhealthy to healthy	Unhealthy to death
Mental state (IO score)	age	↑[1]	↑	↓	↑
	sex	↑F[2]	↑M		↑M
Vision	age		↑	↓	↑
	sex	↑F	↑M		↑M
Hearing	age	↑	↑	↓	↑
	sex		↑M		↑M
Urinary incontinence	age		↑		↑
	sex	↑F	↑M	↑M	
Mobility	age	↑	↑	↓	
	sex	↑F	↑M		
Getting out of doors	age		↑	↓	↑
	sex	↑F	↑M		↑M
Physical ADL scale	age	↑	↑	↓	↑
	sex		↑M		
Katz scale	age		↑		↑
	sex	↑F	↑M		
Self perceived health	age		↑	↓	↑
	sex		↑M		↑M
Depression (SAD scale)	age	↓	↑		↑
	sex	↑F	↑M		↑M
Global health	age		↑	↓	↑
	sex		↑M		↑M
Health Index	age				↑
	sex				↑M

[1] Likelihood of transition significantly increased with increasing age
[2] Likelihood of transition significantly increased for females

Once the $_{ij}\mu$ are obtained, the calculations of the multistate life table follow separately for each sex. From this point, the multistate method is described in more detail in Box 11.1. Almost all the transitions to death from either state are more likely at older ages and for males. A majority of measures show a greater tendency for movement from 'healthy' to 'unhealthy' for women compared to men, whilst there seems little difference between the sexes for movement the other way.

Two types of multistate life tables can be calculated, these being population-based or status based. The former distributes the initial subpopulations according to the observed prevalence of the states in the population whilst the latter distributes the radix population equally between the states. One set of life expectancies independent of initial state can therefore be calculated for the population-based table. The status-based life tables are calculated conditional upon initial state and cannot be combined to produce population-based tables. Population-based tables will be calculated throughout both for comparability with the estimates from the cross-sectional method and since the size of the data sets and the number of transitions between some of the states renders many of the status-based estimates unstable.

The interval between the two waves of the NLSAA was four years whilst the second wave of interview for the MMAP began 57 months after the first sample was drawn. To aid comparison with the cross-sectional estimates, it was assumed that there was an interval of five years between the two waves of each study. This assumption is likely to give slightly higher estimates of total life expectancy and lower healthy life expectancies as fewer transitions take place than would be expected. Estimates of transitions could not be inflated without the unlikely assumption that moves between states had equal probability. Since all subjects were flagged at the National Health Service Central Registry death information is complete but this will tend to reduce life expectancy estimates somewhat as the follow-ups are more likely to miss live persons than dead ones. In addition, as the first wave of the NLSAA did not include any people in institutions, those institutionalised from MMAP were weighted up to represent the combined populations.

11.1   Mental impairment

Life expectancies with mental impairment as defined by a score of 8 or under on the Information/Orientation subtest of the CAPE assessment are shown in Table 11.2. There were a few instances of higher scores at follow-up than initial interview, though this probably reflects the crudeness of the scale as well as the variability of cognitive function that elderly people may have. As shown by the cross-sectional estimates (Table 10.3) women experience a longer residual life with mental impairment than men.

Box 11.1: Calculating health expectancy by multistate life table method

1 Form the matrix $\mathbf{M}_x$ of transition rates at age x as follows

$$\mathbf{M}_x(1,1) = {_{01}}\mu_x + {_{02}}\mu_x, \quad \mathbf{M}_x(1,2) = {-_{10}}\mu_x, \quad \mathbf{M}_x(2,1) = {-_{01}}\mu_x, \quad \mathbf{M}_x(2,2) = {_{10}}\mu_x + {_{12}}\mu_x$$

The diagonal entries of $\mathbf{M}_x$ give the total force of transition out of the state.

2 Calculate
$$\mathbf{P}_x = [\mathbf{I} + 2.5 * \mathbf{M}_x]^{-1}[\mathbf{I} - 2.5 * \mathbf{M}_x]$$

where $\mathbf{P}_x$ are the transition probability matrices. The (ij)th element of $\mathbf{P}_x$, $_{ij}\mathbf{P}_x$, is the probability that a person in state i (i=0,1) at age x will survive and be in state j (j=0,1,2) at age x+5.

3 The familiar life table relationships are now carried forward in matrix notation as follows

$$\mathbf{l}_{x+5} = \mathbf{l}_x.\mathbf{P}_x$$

where $\mathbf{l}_0$ is a diagonal matrix with entries a and b with a=10,000 x proportion observed in state 0 (healthy) in lowest age group at first survey and b=10,000 - a.

4 Calculate
$$\mathbf{L}_x = 2.5 * [\mathbf{l}_x + \mathbf{l}_{x+5}] \qquad i=0,1 \text{ and } x<90$$
and
$$\mathbf{L}_{90} = \mathbf{M}_{90}^{-1}.\mathbf{l}_{90}$$

5 If $_0l_x = {_{00}}l_x + {_{01}}l_x$ denotes the number of survivors in state 0 (healthy) at age x and $_0L_x$ the number of person years lived by these survivors, with $_1l_x$ and $_1L_x$ denoting the equivalent quantities for state 1 (unhealthy). Then the total years lived beyond age x in state i (i=0,1) is given by

$$_iT_x = \Sigma\ _iL_k$$

where the summation is from x to 90.

6 The healthy life expectancy at age x is then given by

$$_0e_x = {_0}T_x / {_0}l_x$$

11.2 Impairments of vision and hearing

Tables 11.3, 11.4 show life expectancies with and without vision and hearing impairments. The percentages of remaining life at each age spent free of impairment were similar to those obtained by the cross-sectional method (Tables 10.4, 10.5). Transitions to visual impairment was significantly greater for women than men. Recoveries to a state of no impairment were greater for hearing than vision with no difference between the sexes. Percentage prevalence of cataract is 34% in men and 47% in women aged 75+ and is the greatest cause of poor vision in this age group. Although prevention is not possible, effective treatment with replacement lens is available and this has been reflected in the high ranking of this operation as a reason for hospital admission (Grimley Evans, 1992).

11.3 Urinary incontinence

Women again experienced a greater proportion of remaining life with incontinence than men. Transitions to and from impairment were more strongly related to sex rather than age with women having a greater likelihood of becoming impaired whilst men were more likely to recover.

11.4 Physical disabilities and impairments of mobility

Estimates using the health states of ability to go out of doors without difficulty or institutionalised, moderate or severe impairment on the Physical Disability Scale and unable to perform one or more ADLs on the Katz scale were available only from the MMAP. Tables 11.6-11.9 confirm that women spend a greater part of their remaining life with disability when compared to men. Though evidence of reversible locomotor disabilities after the provision of aids and adaptations have been found in the UK (George et al, 1988; Hart et al, 1990), the numbers of transitions from dependence back to independence here were extremely low with all three measures and those that did occur were exclusively at the younger ages. For all measures apart from the Physical Disability scale, women were more likely than men to become independent, though there seemed to be little difference between the sexes in transitions back to independence (Table 11.1).

Multistate life expectancies using dependence in one or more ADLs on the Katz scale have been reported from two US studies, though the actual number of ADLs employed in the construction of the scale has varied. In the Massachusetts panel study, people aged 80 years and independent could expect a further 7.6 years of life of which 74% (5.6 years) would be spent in an independent state, whilst those initially dependent had a further 6.5 years, 2.5 of which were spent living independently (Rogers et al, 1989). Rogers also analyzed data from the first two waves of the US Longitudinal Study of Aging (LSOA) and provided estimates of remaining life at 80 years of 7.8 years if initially independent with 4.4 years spent independent and a further 7.7 years if initially dependent, 4.2 of which would be spent independent (Rogers et al, 1990). Grigsby and Bailey (1992) extended this analysis with two further waves of the LSOA and presented population-based multistate active life expectancies separately for men and women. At age 80 men had 5.0 remaining years of which 0.52 years would be spent dependent in one or more ADLs, whilst women of the same age had a further 7.3 years of which 1.1 years would be dependent. Both the Massachusetts study and the LSOA found much higher recovery rates, resulting in higher remaining life independent, due to the much closer time between subsequent waves. The relatively large interval between initial interview and follow-up in both the MMAP and NLSAA results in transitions being missed.

11.5 Self perceived health

Table 11.10 shows the expectation of remaining life in good health. At the individual level the differences between years spent in each state for men and women are more striking than from the cross-sectional population figures. For men at each age around half the remaining years are spent in each

state whilst for women there is a much stronger relationship with age and more years are spent at every age in less than good health. The likelihood of moving from good health to poor and vice versa did not appear to be different for the sexes but improving perceived health was significantly related to age (Table 11.1).

11.6 Depression

A measure of depression at more than one occasion was available only from the NLSAA and hence the calculations in Box 11.1 were slightly modified to take 85 years and over as the final age group. Table 11.11 gives the multistate life expectancies with and without depression as defined by the SAD scale. This was the only measure considered for which transition to a worse state (in this case to depression) was less at older ages, as shown by the increasing proportion with age of remaining life spent free of depression (Table 11.1).

11.7 Global health

As shown by the high prevalence of either mental or physical disability, incontinence or less than good perceived health, much of the remaining lives of both men and women are spent in a state of ill-health as defined by this global health measure (Table 11.12) or the Health Index of the NLSAA (Table 11.13). Despite the tendency for older people to have multiple health problems, these results suggest that 20% of a 70 year old woman's remaining life and 35% of a man's were free of mental and physical disability, incontinence and with good perceived health.

Table 11.2: Expectation of remaining life with and without mental impairment (mental impairment defined as IO score of 8 or under) from population-based multistate life table (MMAP and NLSAA)

| Age (yrs) | Life expectancy (yrs) | | | |
	Total	No impairment	Impaired	Proportion (%) not impaired
Males				
65	13.61	13.26	0.35	97.4
70	10.68	10.40	0.28	97.4
75	8.11	7.86	0.26	96.8
80	6.00	5.76	0.23	96.1
85	4.33	4.12	0.21	95.2
Females				
65	15.94	15.21	0.73	95.4
70	12.67	12.00	0.68	94.6
75	9.81	9.16	0.65	93.4
80	7.41	6.80	0.61	91.8
85	5.50	4.93	0.57	89.6

Table 11.3 Expectation of remaining life with and without visual impairment or institutionalised from population-based multistate life table (MMAP and NLSAA)

| Age (yrs) | Life expectancy (yrs) | | | |
	Total	No impairment	Impaired	Proportion (%) not impaired
Males				
65	13.31	10.19	3.12	76.6
70	10.32	7.60	2.73	73.6
75	7.81	5.57	2.24	71.3
80	5.77	4.03	1.74	69.8
85	4.18	2.90	1.28	69.3
Females				
65	16.27	11.48	4.79	70.6
70	12.89	8.48	4.41	65.8
75	9.99	6.22	3.78	62.2
80	7.59	4.51	3.08	59.4
85	5.69	3.28	2.42	57.5

Table 11.4: Expectation of remaining life with and without hearing impairment or institutionalised from population-based multistate life table (MMAP and NLSAA)

Age (yrs)	Life expectancy (yrs)			
	Total	No impairment	Impaired	Proportion (%) not impaired
Males				
65	13.63	9.09	4.54	66.7
70	10.69	7.06	3.63	66.0
75	8.17	5.28	2.90	64.6
80	6.08	3.81	2.27	62.6
85	4.42	2.68	1.74	60.6
Females				
65	16.30	12.38	3.92	75.9
70	13.00	9.46	3.54	72.7
75	10.12	7.03	3.09	69.4
80	7.70	5.09	2.61	66.1
85	5.76	3.63	2.13	63.1

Table 11.5: Expectation of remaining life with and without urinary incontinence from population-based multistate life table (MMAP and NLSAA)

Age (yrs)	Life expectancy (yrs)			
	Total	Continent	Incontinent	Proportion (%) continent
Males				
65	13.90	12.23	1.67	88.0
70	10.72	9.13	1.58	85.2
75	8.05	6.73	1.32	83.6
80	5.87	4.85	1.02	82.6
85	4.17	3.40	0.77	81.6
Females				
65	15.21	11.52	3.69	75.7
70	11.95	8.81	3.14	73.8
75	9.19	6.71	2.48	73.0
80	6.91	5.06	1.85	73.3
85	5.11	3.80	1.32	74.3

Table 11.6: Expectation of remaining life with and without mobility impairment from population-based multistate life table (MMAP and NLSAA)

Age (yrs)	Life expectancy (yrs)			
	Total	No impairment	Impaired	Proportion (%) not impaired
Males				
65	13.18	12.84	0.34	97.5
70	10.10	9.74	0.35	96.5
75	7.59	7.23	0.34	95.3
80	5.54	5.18	0.37	93.4
85	3.96	3.56	0.39	90.0
Females				
65	15.03	14.47	0.56	96.3
70	11.94	11.10	0.54	95.5
75	9.11	8.55	0.56	93.9
80	6.84	6.29	0.56	91.9
85	5.05	4.48	0.57	88.7

Table 11.7: Expectation of remaining life with and without difficulty getting out of doors or institutionalised from population-based multistate life table (MMAP)

Age (yrs)	Life expectancy (yrs)			
	Total	No difficulty	Difficulty or in institution	Proportion (%) with no difficulty
Males				
75	7.70	5.76	1.95	74.7
80	6.14	4.72	1.43	76.8
85	4.91	3.91	1.00	79.6
Females				
75	9.63	5.73	3.90	59.5
80	7.63	4.38	3.25	57.4
85	6.12	3.49	2.63	57.0

Table 11.8: Expectation of remaining life independent and dependent (dependent defined as moderate or severe physical disability on the Physical ADL scale) from population-based multistate life table (MMAP)

Age (yrs)	Life expectancy (yrs)			
	Total	Independent	Dependent	Proportion (%) independent
Males				
75	7.80	6.52	1.28	83.6
80	5.99	4.93	1.06	82.2
85	4.52	3.59	0.93	79.4
Females				
75	9.44	7.93	1.50	84.1
80	7.48	6.29	1.19	84.1
85	5.83	4.84	0.99	83.0

Table 11.9: Expectation of remaining life independent and dependent (dependent in 1 or more ADLs by the Katz scale) from population-based multistate life table (MMAP)

Age (yrs)	Life expectancy (yrs)			
	Total	Independent	Dependent	Proportion (%) independent
Males				
75	7.41	5.94	1.47	80.2
80	5.62	4.30	1.32	76.5
85	4.29	3.21	1.08	74.9
Females				
75	8.49	6.37	2.12	75.1
80	6.57	4.72	1.85	71.8
85	5.26	3.78	1.48	71.9

Table 11.10: Expectation of remaining life by sex in poor or fair perceived health and good health from population-based multistate life table (MMAP and NLSAA)

Age (yrs)	Life expectancy (yrs)			
	Total	Good health	Less than good health	Proportion (%) in good health
Males				
65	13.53	7.37	6.16	54.4
70	10.41	5.53	4.88	53.1
75	7.79	4.10	3.69	52.7
80	5.67	3.02	2.65	53.3
85	4.03	2.24	1.79	55.6
Females				
65	15.92	7.61	8.31	47.8
70	12.54	5.88	6.66	46.9
75	9.61	4.42	5.19	46.0
80	7.16	3.25	3.91	45.4
85	5.22	2.36	2.86	45.3

Table 11.11: Expectation of remaining life by sex with and without depression from population-based multistate life table (NLSAA)

Age (yrs)	Life expectancy (yrs)			
	Total	Without depression	With depression	Proportion (%) depression free
Males				
65	14.15	9.12	5.04	64.4
70	10.55	7.96	2.60	75.4
75	8.18	7.23	0.95	88.3
80	7.86	7.79	0.07	99.0
Females				
65	17.94	15.14	2.80	84.4
70	14.27	12.24	2.03	85.8
75	11.14	9.99	1.15	89.7
80	9.19	8.79	0.40	95.7

Table 11.12: Expectation of remaining life by sex with and without global health from population-based multistate life table (MMAP and NLSAA)

Age (yrs)	Life expectancy (yrs)			
	Total	With health	Without health	Proportion (%) healthy
Males				
65	13.81	6.64	7.08	48.8
70	10.86	3.76	6.86	35.4
75	5.77	2.21	5.77	27.6
80	4.48	1.37	4.48	23.5
85	3.29	0.94	3.29	22.2
Females				
65	15.85	3.53	12.32	22.3
70	12.56	2.46	10.10	19.6
75	9.72	1.74	7.98	17.9
80	7.37	1.27	6.10	17.2
85	5.52	0.98	4.54	17.7

Table 11.13: Expectation of remaining life by sex with and without health (defined by Health Index) from population-based multistate life table (NLSAA)

Age (yrs)	Life expectancy (yrs)			
	Total	With health	Without health	Proportion (%) healthy
Males				
65	13.11	4.12	8.98	31.5
70	10.64	1.52	9.12	14.2
75	7.64	0.58	7.05	7.6
80	5.11	0.28	4.82	5.5
Females				
65	14.12	4.35	9.78	30.8
70	11.88	1.60	10.29	13.5
75	8.80	0.60	8.20	6.8
80	6.10	0.27	5.83	4.5

12 Health expectancy and the need for national longitudinal data

In the remaining chapters of this report we argue the case for establishing a national longitudinal database for measuring health expectancy generally and for monitoring trends in the incidence of health events. We begin by summarising the demographic developments which underline the need for long-term planning of health and social care resources, and then outline the features of a health expectancy indicator which could aid the process.

Population aging in Great Britain is projected to continue for over 40 years. By 2041 people aged 65 or more will form one quarter of the population, compared with the present 16%. Part of the growth in the elderly population over this century is undoubtedly due to increases in the expectation of life at age 65, which is still averaging an increase of one year per decade. The prevalence of chronic disease and disability increase with age, and if the age specific prevalence of disability seen in 1985 were to continue unchanged, the numbers of people with disabilities of some degree in 2031 would be 9 million - 3 million more than in 1985.

Scientific advances and other changes may either increase or diminish the extent of infirmity among the elderly. One view is that people now in early middle age will have a greater chance than their predecessors of living out their lives in relatively good health until the very end. Morbidity would then be compressed into a short period before death and so become less prevalent than today (Fries, 1980). The contrasting pessimistic view is that increasing preservation of many who would formerly have died at younger ages will multiply numbers of the unfit and result in a 'pandemic' of mental disorders and chronic diseases - an expansion of morbidity (Kramer, 1980; Gruenberg, 1977). The evidence so far from this and other industrialised countries suggests an expansion of the volume of light to moderate disabilities, but compression of that of the most severe disabilities. This evidence is however compromised by the lack of longitudinal data, the implications of which are described below.

Health expectancy provides a means of monitoring developments. Health expectancy is like life expectancy but refers to the further years of good health people of a given age can on average expect to enjoy. It thus combines mortality and morbidity into a single index in a way which is independent of the age structure of the population to which it relates. Health expectancy is the generic term, and specific forms are, for example, disability-free life expectancy, dementia-free life expectancy and dependency-free life expectancy. The appropriate measure depends on the purpose for which it is to be used. The complement of health expectancy is ill-health expectancy - the number of years people of a given age can expect to live in poor health.

Figures in earlier chapters show, for example, that women aged 75 in 1991 could on average expect to live for about 11.5 more years, 5 of which would be spent without, and just over 6 with, any limiting long-standing illness (Census 1991 definition). These levels appear to have remained fairly stationary between 1976 and 1991 whilst expectation of life independent in basic self-care for women aged 75 appears to have increased from 6.5 years in 1976 (67% of total life expectancy) to 10.0 years (90% of total life expectancy) in 1991. When a range of disabilities and impairments are considered, deterioration from 'healthy' to 'unhealthy' states is more likely for women than men and the chance of recovery decreases significantly with increasing age. Impairments of hearing and vision make the greatest impact on health expectancy, with women aged 75 spending 30% of their remaining years with these conditions.

Health expectancy can be used to monitor trends in the health status of the population over time and so to indicate the broad impact of health and social policy. It can also be used: to compare the health of populations and subgroups as an aid to resource allocation; to estimate the effects on population health of different intervention strategies, and so contribute to the identification of priorities for intervention; and to project the health status of the population under different assumptions as an aid to resource planning for the short and longer term future.

Most commonly, health expectancy has been calculated from mortality figures together with cross-sectional data on the prevalence of morbidity which are widely available from surveys and, sometimes, censuses. The use of prevalence data assumes that people of a given age will later experience the same prevalence of morbidity as those older than themselves. This is unsatisfactory because current prevalence depends on the past history of the population; for example, the decline in smoking means that younger cohorts will not experience the same prevalence of smoking related diseases and consequent disability as those now in their 60s and 70s. A truer picture of the way the health status of the population is evolving is given by incidence rates - the rates at which people are currently becoming ill or improving, and more generally, by the *rates of transition* between health states. It is these rates which drive the future evolution of prevalence rates, and which are affected by interventions long before the impact on prevalence is manifested. Transition rates are therefore essential for making projections and will produce much better and more informative estimates than prevalence rates of the effect of health care interventions. In general, it is only if transition rates remain stable over a very long period - several generations - that cross-sectional prevalence data will yield measures of health expectancy which are adequate for the policy applications described. As was shown in Chapter 3, such stability is unlikely.

Transition rates are derived from longitudinal data, but at present no longitudinal data of the right kind exist in this country at the national level. The following chapters spell out the case for establishing a national longitudinal data base. We first describe the kind of longitudinal data required, consider potential sources of such data and the extent to which each may be expected to meet the requirements. Finally, we make recommendations about the next steps which need to be taken if it is agreed that a longitudinal database should be set up.

13 The kind of longitudinal data required

The key feature of a longitudinal health data set which should determine its selection or design, is the estimation of the *incidence* of health events: the age/sex-specific transition rates between states of health at a point in time.

Consequently, longitudinal data here mean data about each of a series of individuals obtained at successive points in time. In practice, the data have often been derived from a longitudinal survey of a single cohort (that is a group of people who were born during the same period, e.g. week, year or five years). For the purposes described in the previous section, what is required is a routine national longitudinal survey or recording system based on a sample of everyone above a given age, including those living in communal establishments. This should either be repeated, with selection of an entirely new sample at regular periods with a single follow-up of each sample, or continuous, with regular follow-ups from the sample and new cohorts coming in as they reach the specified age (as in the US National Long-Term Care Survey (NLTCS), further described in chapter 14). Results on health expectancy and related information from cross-sectional data, including prevalence figures (e.g. on disability, dependency and specific conditions) would be available from the second system from the time material from the first data collection occasion - or wave - had been analysed onwards. Longitudinal evidence of transition rates allowing calculation of true period health expectancy, projections and the potential effect of interventions would be produced from the first consecutive pair of waves and each following pair.

13.1 Sample size and follow-up period

Sample size is mentioned in the next chapter on the basis of particular assumptions. In particular, the appropriate size would depend at least on:

- the expected incidence of the events of interest. Results for specific health conditions will require a larger sample than would general health measures;

- whether results were required at district, regional, or only at national level. As policy making and service provision has now been devolved down to districts, changes in health expectancy should be detectable at this level;

- whether results were required for the whole population or just for elderly people;

- the extent to which results were needed for separate socio-economic, ethnic or other subgroups of the population (as well as by age and sex) in order to monitor equity in health and social care;

- the smallest change over time, or difference between subgroups, which would be of interest.

It is, however, clear that, whatever the purposes, a fairly substantial sample would be needed, given that numbers dwindle with age, and particularly in the case of men. As a guide, the US NLTCS has a sample size of approximately 34,000 persons aged 65 years and over for the first wave in 1982 and 23,000 for the 1984 and 1989 waves. Each sample included around 2,000 in the oldest (85+) age group and aimed to identify at least 6,000 chronically disabled older persons.

The interval between waves must be sufficiently long for enough health events to allow good estimates of transition rates, but not so long that multiple transitions will obscure these estimates. The follow-up period may be dependent on the age of the subject. The optimum period for elderly people may be as brief as one to two years (Brouard, 1994).

13.2 Criteria to be met by required data base source

These are as follows:

- Longitudinal data on individuals of all ages from the specified minimum
- Provision for new cohorts to 'age-in' to the database as they reach the minimum age
- Nationally representative of all individuals from the minimum age
- Residents of communal establishments to be included
- Adequate numbers of the smallest main subgroup (e.g. males aged 85+)
- Sufficiently frequent data collection occasions to capture most transitions of interest
- Includes youngest age of interest
- Standardised disability data collected
- All diagnosed conditions included
- Mortality data on individuals included or available
- Sample members who move are followed up
- Information on use of all health and personal social services collected
- Socio-economic data on individuals collected

In the next chapter we assess how well some potentially available data sources meet these criteria.

14   Review of possible data sources

We considered six possible sources of longitudinal data of the kind required. They are:

- OPCS Longitudinal Study
- GP annual health check of people aged 75 and over
- General Practice Research Database (GPRD)
- GPRD plus interviews
- Purpose designed longitudinal survey
- GHS or English Health Survey with added longitudinal element

All sources but the first and the last could potentially yield all the measures listed earlier: cross-sectional estimates of health expectancy based on prevalence data; period estimates of health expectancy based on incidence/transition rates; and cohort estimates of health expectancy. A longitudinal element added to the GHS or English Health Survey, as described here, would allow estimation of the first two, but not the last. Key features of each source and its advantages and disadvantages are considered below and the results of our assessment are summarised in Table 14.1 at the end of this chapter.

14.1 OPCS Longitudinal Study (LS)

The LS was set up in the late sixties to provide more reliable and extensive statistics on mortality than are otherwise available. Longitudinal event data are maintained for a very large sample of 500,000 people of all ages. The information is derived by linking data on individuals from successive censuses since 1971 and relating them to event data (e.g. on births and deaths) held by OPCS for the same individuals. Samples of new births and immigrants are added each year. The large sample size allows detailed analysis of comparatively small subpopulations, including those of (or moving between) small geographical areas. The information it can yield, however, is necessarily restricted by the limited number of questions asked and repeated in successive censuses and by the few events which are registerable. It is not available as a sample source for a survey because the data on individuals are protected by legislation (Census Act, 1920). For present purposes, therefore, it has value only as a supplementary source of information, but could not provide sufficiently detailed material on morbidity and transitions between health states to be the main source. It is therefore not included in the assessment in Table 14.1.

14.2 GP annual surveillance of the elderly

In 1990, the new GP contract was introduced (Department of Health, 1989). One of the statutory elements included was that general practitioners should offer an annual health check, at home, for their patients aged 75 years and over and a triennial check for the next age group down, 65-74 year olds. Broad guidelines on the areas of assessment were provided

(social, mobility, mental, hearing, vision, continence) but no specific instruments were proposed.

Grimley Evans (1993) proposed that Healthy Active Life Expectancy at the ADL level as a proportion of total life expectancy might be increased by 1.5% per annum over a decade for ages 65, 75 and 85. Rough calculations on the cohort size to detect such differences were made based on the cross-sectional estimates for women from chapter 10. An initial cohort of around 7,500 would reduce the standard errors on disability-free life expectancy at age 75 to around 0.04 years, sufficient to detect the proposed increases at this age, though not at older ages. The average list size per GP in England in 1991 was 1,947 persons of whom an estimated 136 (7%) would be aged 75 years and over. The average practice size is a partnership of 4 doctors, so that the average practice would have around 550 patients aged 75 years and over. Hence, around 15 general practices would produce a cohort of 7,500 aged 75 years and over.

It is unlikely that the same efforts to maximise response rates will be sustained in annual assessments as in one-off surveys, though response rates may themselves increase as surveillance becomes an accepted part of practice policy. Analysis of the first year assessments in Melton Mowbray (response rate 67%) suggest that those who did not take up the offer of an assessment were very similar to those accepting the assessment on a variety of demographic and health characteristics (Jagger et al, 1995).

Advantages

1 Panel design with one year between waves, thus missing few transitions.
2 Cross-sectional estimates can also be calculated.
3 Institutional residents included as they are not deregistered from the practice lists unless in long-stay geriatric or psychiatric hospital care (a diminishing area of care).
4 Potential to link with other computer-based GP information such as diagnosis.

Disadvantages

1 Would require standardisation of assessments between practices.
2 Response rates are unlikely to be as high as in one-off surveys.
3 Disability-free life expectancy only at 75 and older. Could include triennial screens of 64-74 year olds but this is less well established.
4 GPs could be sampled so that the patient population was representative of England and Wales, but the sample would be too small to assess district, regional and subgroup differences.

14.3 General Practice Research Database (GPRD)

OPCS is currently developing, for the Department of Health, a central database of information on individuals derived from 660 GP practices using the VAMP computer system. The practices cover over 4 million patients - that is, everyone on the practice lists whatever their age, and including the new-born. This initial system is in operation and data are transferred to the database once a month. The Department has been reviewing various options for consolidating collection of health data from general practice, which could potentially lead to coverage of a large number of practices. It is likely that any extension would be designed to ensure that the patients of these practices were representative of the whole population - except that of long-stay hospitals, which is not covered by GPs. Currently, the OXMIS/ICD 8 system of classifying diseases is being used; later, there will be a move to READ/ICD 10, which will bring it into line with the most recent revision of the International Classification of Diseases (ICD).

There are, in principle, two ways in which the GPRD could be used:

As a data source only; the data in the system could be used directly (after a pilot study to check validity) to calculate different specific health expectancies and related measures by the multistate method. Information from the 75+ health checks should be included, and if these cover ADLs and other evidence of morbidity in a standard form (as a result of the MRC trial of assessment and management of elderly people in the community) then it would be possible to calculate disability-free life expectancy based on ADLs and specific types of morbidity for this age group.

As a data source and sampling frame for an interview survey; the system could be used both to provide data on morbidity and as a frame from which to draw a sample (with replenishment) for repeated interviewing by professional interviewers. Interviews would provide systematic information on disabilities and handicaps; on use of personal assistance, equipment and services; as well as on socio-economic circumstances, etc. - questions which it might be difficult for GPs or practice nurses to ask. Sample members who had moved could be followed up in the normal way and through the NHSCR.

It will be seen that, in effect, the second results in a multi-cohort longitudinal survey with aging-in of new cohorts. The advantage, compared with other ways of producing a sample, would be that data from interviews could be linked with GP data on diagnosed conditions. In addition, if required, younger cohorts could be added.

The question marks attach to:

- whether, in fact, patients included in the system will be representative of the whole population;

- whether it would receive clearance from ethical committees;

- what proportion of practices selected for the sample would agree to contact selected patients to ask for their agreement to participate in the survey;

- whether there would be any other data protection problems;

- how soon the complete system will be in place.

The advantages and disadvantages listed below relate to this second option which includes interviewing.

Advantages
1 Would make use of an existing data collection system.
2 Continuous data on morbidity available from the system.
3 Cross-sectional and longitudinal (period and cohort) estimates can be made.
4 Institutional residents included unless in long-stay geriatric or psychiatric hospitals.
5 No restriction on minimum age.
6 Questions on disability, handicap, use of aids and personal social services would be asked in standardised form by interviewers.
7 Information about socio-economic and other relevant circumstances can be obtained from subjects or their carers.
8 Those who move can be followed up.

Disadvantages
1 People in long-stay hospitals excluded.
2 The uncertainties listed earlier.

14.4 Purpose designed free-standing multicohort longitudinal survey

One possible model for a multicohort longitudinal study is the US National Long-Term Care Survey (NLTCS). This survey, with waves in 1982, 1984 and 1989, uses as its sampling frame the administrative records for all persons aged 65 years and over eligible for Medicare (almost all the total population of this age). The survey waves are two stage with an initial screening phase followed by a detailed home interview with those found to be chronically disabled. The first wave screened only those living in the community, though subsequent waves have included those in institutional care as well as following up survivors from previous waves and a sample of those achieving age 65 between waves. Response rates have been over 95% in all waves though the ability to link the sample drawn with Medicare records provides much data on non-responders. Sample weights have been constructed to account for non-response and other sampling design factors as well as to reproduce the US population figures. The sample size of the NLTCS has been discussed in chapter 13.

Evidence of the actual lifetime health expectancy of cohorts of people aged 65 or more would emerge from such a survey after about ten years. The point at which the three types of result would first be available, where annual data collection waves are assumed, is shown below:

1st year Wave Health expectancy calculated from cross-sectional data on prevalence (period measure)

2nd year Wave Health expectancy calculated from data on transitions occurring between 1st and 2nd waves (period measure)

3rd year Wave Time series of period measures of health expectancy

10th year Wave First cohort measures of health expectancy

A free-standing survey would avoid all the restrictions imposed by being combined with other investigations. For example it could be designed to combine people in communal establishments with those living at home. It would not be dependent on the cooperation of GPs and could cover people who rarely visit them. This would of course mean that medical records would not be available. The survey would rely on self-reported information as in the GB Disability Surveys of 1986-8, though physical measurements and analysis of specimens might be included as in the English Health Survey (Bennett et al 1995). A postal survey is unlikely to be satisfactory. It is worth noting that the US NLTCS, described above, was designed as a free-standing interview survey.

The main drawback of a free-standing survey is that the cost is likely to be high compared with a 'piggy-back' survey. This is largely because of the necessary sampling procedures. A complication with a 'replenishment' design like that of the NLTCS is that there would have to be continued selection from the sampling frame of respondents as younger cohorts 'age in'. There are three choices for the sampling frame:

- A general survey of households and institutions, using standard selection procedures. This would be suitable if all the population were to be included, but expensive if the survey were to concentrate on just elderly people.

- There appears to be one suitable non-GP based frame for elderly people: the DSS record of those eligible for state pensions. However under Data Protection legislation individuals would have to be first contacted by the DSS, and this might result in a poor response rate.

- The GPRD. This has already been described. It omits those people not registered with GP's or in long-stay hospitals. The advantages and disadvantages listed below therefore relate to the first two options above only.

Advantages
1   Cover people who rarely visit, or who are not registered with GPs.

2   Cover people in all health related communal establishments, including long-stay hospitals.
3   Not dependent on cooperation of health professionals.

Disadvantages
1   The only suitable sampling frame (DSS) is likely to yield very low response.
2   Only self-reported morbidity likely to be obtainable.

14.5 Extending an existing continuous national survey

Another possibility is to add a longitudinal element to an existing survey which is sufficiently large for this purpose, is nationally representative, and which is suitable for including questions about health. The most likely contenders for this are the General Household Survey and the English Health Survey.

The General Household Survey (GHS) is a continuous nationally representative interview survey of private households including about 25,000 individuals of whom around 4,000 are over 65. Results are produced annually. There is a regular short section on health and use of health services, to which is added about every 5 years a more detailed section on disability of elderly people. About 5,000 individuals (1,750 over 65) report themselves as having a limiting long-standing illness.

The English Health Survey is similarly an annual nationally representative survey of private households, from which people over 16 are interviewed and surveyed. From 1993 on the sample size has been approximately 17,000: a similar size to the GHS except excluding children. (From 1995 children will be included in the English Health Survey.) The survey includes questions on specific health conditions, but these vary from year to year.

Both surveys provide moderately large samples of people who in principle could be re-visited after a period of time. The sample size in each case would be sufficient to provide accurate estimation of health expectancy based on transitions/incidence at least for major subgroups of elderly people. A possible design using the GHS would be to follow up elderly people from every third annual survey once after a period of three years. It is not necessarily the case that all elderly people would be re-contacted: the information from the main survey could be used to guide the selection of cases for optimum estimation efficiency. This would probably mean over-sampling of those who were identified as having health problems at the first interview - although the scope for over-sampling is limited by the size of the GHS itself. Possibly two years' samples might be combined.

This design would provide a time series of period health expectancies at three-yearly intervals, but would not generate long-term data on individuals or real cohorts. Its main advantage is that, apart from coverage of communal establishments, such a study could be set up quickly and easily compared with the other possible sources considered.

Table 14.1: Criteria for assessing options for longitudinal data

Criteria	GP annual health check	GPRD	GPRD plus interviewing	Health survey/ GHS with longitudinal element	Purpose designed longitudinal survey
Longitudinal data on individuals	yes	yes	yes	yes	yes
Aging-in of new cohorts	yes	yes	yes	yes	yes
Nationally representative	?	?	?	yes	yes
Communal estabs included	yes, but excludes long stay hospitals	yes, but excludes long stay hospitals	yes, but excludes long stay hospitals	no	yes
Adequate nos. of males ages 85+ for further disaggregation	yes	yes	yes	no	yes
Youngest age included	75	under 1 yr	under 1 yr	65	as required
Frequency of data collection	annual	monthly	?	3-yearly	?
Standardised disability data	?	?	yes	yes	yes
Morbidity data a) all diagnosed b) standardised	a) ? b) ?	a) yes b) ?	a) yes b) ?	no	no
Mortality data of individuals	yes	yes	yes	yes	yes
Movers followed up	no	no	yes	yes	yes
Other service use	yes	no	yes	yes	yes
Socio-economic etc data	no	no	yes	yes	yes

Advantages
1   Could be mounted quickly and easily compared with other options.
2   Not being dependent on co-operation from health professionals.
3   Having the established reliability of existing mainstream surveys, particularly in relation to representativeness and quality of response.

Disadvantages
1   These surveys exclude people not living in private households, for whom a separate sub-survey would have to be organised.
2   There would be non-response at the follow up and some effort would be necessary to ensure that deaths were identified.
3   The surveys are too small for detailed local or subgroup estimates.

14.6   Conclusion

Results of the assessment of potential sources of longitudinal data are summarised in Table 14.1. The sources discussed are of three kinds: those originating from GPs; those produced by interview surveys and those that result from a combination of the two. The first kind are likely to be based - at least for patients aged 75 or over - on assessments and measurements made by practice nurses as well as on laboratory tests, and have the obvious advantage that they will or may include diagnoses provided by clinicians. It is not yet clear, however, to what extent assessments and measurements will be standardised over all practices throughout the country.

Interview surveys, on the other hand, must rely largely on self-reported health problems and diagnoses (although physical measurements and laboratory tests are sometimes included). Assessments and physical measurements, however, will be rigorously standardised and the greatest advantage of surveys is that they will or can include systematic information on socio-economic and other circumstances and on use of other services which may not be appropriately collected by GPs or practice nurses.

Clearly, other things being equal, an approach which combines the advantages of both types of data will be the preferred source. So, the GPRD - or indeed the GP Annual Health Check - supplemented by interviews by professional interviewers using purpose-designed standard questionnaires would yield the richest information; in principle, the data produced could be used to address all the policy issues listed earlier.

Either source without interviewing would provide some of the material needed, but its value would be much greater than otherwise if key information were obtained and recorded in a standardised form. Socio-economic data are unlikely to be included.

A longitudinal element added to the GHS or English Health Survey could also yield answers to some of the policy questions outlined earlier, but only if a complementary survey of communal establishments were added, and both have rather small samples of older people for some purposes.

The best source of longitudinal data from among those listed, however, depends on the specific purposes for which it is to be used. As we have indicated, the time when any of the sources might be available is uncertain, the cost of using any in this way is at present unknown, and each of them would require development if it were to be selected. It is not possible, therefore, to recommend one rather than another at this stage. In the next section we outline the next steps which would be necessary to arrive at a decision on which source to use and to ensure that it could be used.

15   Recommendations

We showed in the first chapter that population aging is projected to continue for at least 40 years. We have outlined some of the main issues this raises and the way that health expectancy and allied measures could contribute to planning resources for health and other services to meet the consequences. At the most fundamental level, health expectancy is a necessary tool for accurate monitoring of the "Health of the Nation". We argue that longitudinal data provide a more reliable basis than the usual cross-sectional data for most of these purposes and that for some they are essential.

The best database will depend on the priority purposes for which it is to be used, its accessibility and the extent to which the data which might flow from it can be standardised, selected and collated so as to serve these purposes - as well as the cost in relation to the expected benefits. If it is agreed that the value of establishing a longitudinal database on the health of the population or of older people should be further considered, then the following steps would be necessary:

1   Agreement on the main policy issues and specific questions to be addressed by the study.

2   Initial design, timetabling and costing of the most promising option(s) given the information required.

3   Decisions and negotiations with data owners to ensure that data from the selected sources will be accessible when needed in the form required (e.g. nationally representative sample, data in standardised form).

4   Detailed study design, timetabling and costing and any further negotiations on access to chosen data source.

References

Applegate, W.B., Hughes, J.P., & Van der Zwaag, R.V. (1991). Case-control study of coronary heart disease risk factors in the elderly. *Journal of Clinical Epidemiology*,**44**,409-415.

Balarajan, R. and Bulusu, L. (1989). Mortality among immigrants in England and Wales, 1979-83. Chapter 9 of Britton, M. (ed) *Mortality and Geography*. OPCS Series DS no. 9.

Barendregt, J.J., Bonneux, L. & van der Maas P.J. (1994). Health expectancy, an indicator for change? *Journal of Epidemiology and Community Health*,**48**,482-7.

Beaglehole, R. (1991). Coronary heart disease and elderly people: no mass treatment of risk factors yet. *British Medical Journal*,**303**,69-70.

Bebbington, A.C. (1988). The expectation of life without disability in England and Wales. *Social Science in Medicine*,**27**,321-326.

Bebbington, A. & Miles, J. (1988). A need indicator for in-care services for children. *PSSRU Discussion Paper No. 574.*

Bebbington, A.C. (1991). The expectation of life without disability in England and Wales: 1976-1988. *Population Trends*,**66**,26-29.

Bebbington, A.C.(1992) Expectation of life measured from the OPCS Disability Surveys. In Robine JM, Blanchet M, Dowd JE,eds. *Health Expectancy* (OPCS series SMPS, No 54). London; HMSO,1992.

Bedford, A., Foulds, G.A. & Sheffield, B.F. (1976). A new personal disturbance scale: DSSi/Sad. *British Journal of Social and Clinical Psychology*,**15**,387-94.

Bennett N., Dodd T., Flatley J., Freeth S., & Bolling K., (1995). *Health Survey for England* 1993. London: HMSO.

Bone, M. & Meltzer, H. (1989). *The prevalence of disability among children; OPCS surveys of disability in Great Britain.* (Report 3) London: HMSO.

Bone, M. (1992). A multi-cohort longitudinal study. In Robine, J.M., Blanchet, M. & Dowd, J.E.,eds. *Health Expectancy* (OPCS series SMPS, No 54). London ; HMSO,1992.

Bone, M.R. (1992). International efforts to measure health expectancy. *Journal of Epidemiology and Community Health*,**46**,555-8.

Boon, N.A. (1991). New deal for old hearts: age alone should not be a barrier to treatment. *British Medical Journal*,**303**,70.

Boshuizen, H.C. (1993). International comparability of health expectancy calculations: aims of the project. In Robine J.M., Mathers C.D., Bone M.R., Romieu I.,eds. *Calculation of health expectancies: harmonization, consensus achieved and future perspectives*; London: John Libbey & Company Ltd.

Boshuizen, H.C., van de Water, H.P.A. & Perenboom, R.M. (1994). Socio-economic differences in health expectancy in the Netherlands. *The 7th International Meeting of the Network on Healthy Life Expectancy (REVES)* Canberra 1994. (to be published)

Britton, M. (1989). Geographic variation in mortality, 1979-83. Chapter 9 of Britton, M. (ed) *Mortality and Geography*. OPCS Series DS no. 9.

Britton, M., Fox, A.J., Goldblatt, P.O., Jones, D.R. & Rosato, M. (1989) The influence of socio-economic and environmental factors on geographic variation in mortality. Chapter 9 of Britton, M. (ed) Mortality and Geography. OPCS Series DS no. 9.

Brouard, N. (1994). Optimal delay between two waves of a longitudinal health survey according to the age of subjects. In: *7th Work-group meeting REVES, International Research Network for Interpretation of Observed Values of Healthy Life Expectancy*, Canberra.

Campbell Stern, M., Jagger, C., Clarke, M. et al. (1993). Residential care for elderly people: a decade of change. *British Medical Journal*,**306**,827-30.

Carr-Hill, R.A., Maynard, A. & Slack R. (1990). Morbidity variation and RAWP. *Journal of Epidemiology and Community Health*,**44**,271-3.

Carr-Hill, R.A., Hardman, G., Martin, S, Peacock, S, Sheldon, T.A. & Smith, P. (1994). *A formula for distributing NHS revenues based on small area use of hospital beds.* CHE, University of York.

Casper, M., Wing, S., Strogatz, D., Davis, C.E., & Tyroler, H.A. (1992). Antihypertensive treatment and US trends in stroke mortality. *American Journal of Public Health*,**82**, 1600-1606.

Christie, A.B., Wood, E.R.M. (1990). Further change in the pattern of mental illness in the elderly. *British Journal of Psychiatry*,**157**,228-231.

Clarke, M., Clarke, S.J., Odell, A. & Jagger, C. (1984). The elderly at home: health and social status. *Health Trends*,**16**,3-7.

Clarke, M., Jagger, C., Anderson, J., Battcock, T., Kelly, F. & Campbell Stern, M. (1991). The prevalence of dementia in a total population - the comparison of two screening instruments. *Age and Aging*,**20**,396-403.

Corder, L.S., Woodbury, M. & Manton, K.G. (1993). Health loss due to unobserved morbidity: a design based approach to minimize nonsampling error in active life expectation estimates. In Robine J.M., Mathers C.D., Bone M.R., Romieu I.,eds. *Calculation of health expectancies: harmonization, consensus achieved and future perspectives*; London: John Libbey & Company Ltd.

Crimmins, E., Saito, Y. & Ingegneri, D. (1989). Changes in life expectancy and disability-free life expectancy in the United States. *Population Development Review*,**15**,235-67.

Crimmins, E., Hayward, M.D. & Saito, Y. (1992a). The relationship between changing mortality rates, changing morbidity rates and the health status of the population. REVES Paper No. 91, presented to *5th International Meeting of the Network on Health Life Expectancy (REVES)*, Ottawa.

Crimmins, E., Saito, Y. & Hayward, M. (1992b). Sullivan and multistate methods of estimating active life expectancy: two methods, two answers. In: *Calculation of health expectancies: harmonization, consensus achieved and future perspectives*. Eds Robine J-M, Mather CD, Bone MR, Romieu I. Colloque INSERM/John Libbey Eurotext Ltd., **226**,155 -160.

Crimmins, E.M., Saito, Y. & Hayward, M.D. (1994). Differentials in active life expectancy in the U.S. population. *The 7th International Meeting of the Network on Healthy Life Expectancy (REVES)* Canberra 1994. (to be published)

Darton, R. & Wright, K. (1993). Changes in the provision of long-stay care, 1970-1990. *Health and Social Care*,**1**,11-25.

Deeg, D.J.H., Kriegsman, D.M.W., van Zonneveld, R.J. (1994) Trends in morbidity and disability 1956-1992 and projections of active life expectancy in the Netherlands. *The 7th International Meeting of the Network on Healthy Life Expectancy (REVES)* Canberra 1994. (to be published)

Department of Health and the Welsh Office. (1989). *General practice in the National Health Service: a new contract.* London: HMSO.

Department of Health. (1992). *Health of the Nation: a strategy for health in England.* London, HMSO.

Farnsworth, T.A., & Heseltine, D. (1993). Treatment of elderly hypertensives: some questions remain unanswered. *Age and Aging*,**22**,1-4.

Folstein, M.F., Folstein, S.E. & McHugh, P.R. (1975). 'Mini-Mental State': a practical method for grading the cognitive state of patients for the clinician. *Journal of Psychiatric Research*,**12**,189-98.

Fries, J.F. (1980). Aging, natural death, and the compression of morbidity. *New England Journal of Medicine*, **31**(3), 407-428.

Goddard, E., & Savage, D. (1994). *People aged 65 years and over: a study carried out on behalf of the Department of Health as part of the 1991 General Household Survey.* London, HMSO.

Grigsby, J.S. & Bailey, D. (1992). Alternative definitions of functional life expectancy. In Robine J.M., Mathers C.D., Bone M.R., Romieu I.,eds. *Calculation of health expectancies: harmonization, consensus achieved and future perspectives*; London: John Libbey & Company Ltd.

Grimley Evans, J. (1991). Aging and rationing: physiology not age should determine care. *British Medical Journal*,**303**,869-70.

Grimley Evans, J., Goldacre, M., Hodkinson, M. et al. (1992). The Carnegie Inquiry into the Third Age, Research Paper Number 9. *Health: Abilities and wellbeing in the Third age.* Fife: The Carnegie United Kingdom Trust.

Grimley Evans, J. (1993). Hypothesis: Healthy Active Life Expectancy (HALE) as an index of effectiveness of health and social services for elderly people. *Age and Aging*,**22**,297-301.

Gruenberg, E.M. (1977). Failures of success. *Millbank Quarterly/Health and Society*,**55**,3-24.

Haberman, S. (1983). Decrement tables and the measurement of morbidity. *Journal of the Institute of Actuaries*,**110**:361-381.

Heathcote, C.R. & McDermid, I.M. (1994) Projections of cohort life expectancy based on weighted least squares methods. *The 7th International Meeting of the Network on Healthy Life Expectancy (REVES)* Canberra 1994. (to be published)

Hermanson, B., Omenn, G.S., Kronmal, R.A., & Gersh, B.J. (1988). Beneficial six-year outcome of smoking cessation in older men and women with coronary artery disease. *New England Journal of Medicine*,**319**,1365-1369.

Isaacs, B. & Neville, Y. (1976). *The measurement of need in old people.* Scottish health Service Studies no. 34. Edinburgh: Scottish Home and Health Department.

ISIS-2 (second international study of infarct survival) Collaborative Group. (1988). Randomised trial of intravenous streptokinase, oral aspirin, both or neither among 17187 cases of suspected acute myocardial infarction: ISIS-2. *Lancet*,(ii),349-60.

Jagger, C., Clarke, M. & Davies, R.A. (1984). The elderly at home: indices of disability. *Journal of Epidemiology and Community Health*,**40**,139-42.

Jagger, C. & Clarke, M. (1988). Mortality risks in the elderly: five year follow-up of a total population. *International Journal of Epidemiology*,**17**,111-114.

Jagger, C., Clarke, M. & Cooke, A.J. (1989). Mental and physical health of elderly people: five-year follow-up of a total population. *Age and Aging*,**18**,77-82.

Jagger, C., Clarke, M. & Clarke, S.J. (1991). Getting older feeling younger - the changing health profile of the elderly. *International Journal of Epidemiology*,**20**,234-8.

Jagger, C. & Clarke, M. (1991). The changing disability profile of the elderly. In: *4th Work-group meeting REVES, International Research Network for Interpretation of Observed Values of Healthy Life Expectancy*, Noordwijkerhout.

Jagger, C., Clarke, M. & Anderson, J. (1992a). Screening for dementia - a comparison of two tests using Receiver Operating Characteristic (ROC) analysis. *International Journal of Geriatric Psychiatry*,**7**,659-665.

Jagger, C., Clarke, M., Anderson, J. & Battcock, T. (1992b). Misclassification of dementia by the Mini-Mental State Examination - are education and social class the only factors? *Age and Aging*,**21**,404-11.

Jagger, C., Spiers, N.A. & Clarke, M. (1993). Factors associated with decline in function, institutionalization and mortality of elderly people. *Age and Aging*,**22**,190-7.

Jagger, C., Clarke, M., O'Shea, C. & Gannon, M. Annual visits to patients over the age of seventy-five - who is missed? (submitted for publication).

Katz, S. & Akpom, C. (1976). A measure of primary socio-biological functions. *International Journal of Health Services*,**6**,493-507.

Katz, S. & Akpom, C.A. (1976). Index of ADL. *Medical Care*, XIV (5) Supplement.

Katz, S., Ford, A.B., Moskowitz, R.W., Jackson B.A. & Jaffe M.W. (1963). Studies of illness in the aged. *Journal of the American Medical Association*,

Katz, S., Branch, L.G., Branson, M.H. et al. (1983). Active life expectancy. *New England Journal of Medicine*,**309**,1218-24.

Knight, T., Smith, Z., Lockton, J.A. et al. (1993). Ethnic differences in risk markers for heart disease in Bradford and implications for preventative strategies. *Journal of Epidemiology and Community Health*,**47**,89-95.

Kramer, M. (1980). The rising pandemic of mental disorders and associated chronic diseases and disabilities. *Acta Psychiatrica Scandinavica*,285,382-397.

Langhorne, P., Williams, B.O., Gilchrist, W., & Howie, K. (1993). Do stroke units save lives? *Lancet*,**342**,395-398.

Ledent, J. (1980). Multistate life tables: movement versus transition perspectives. *Environment and Planning A*,**12**,533-562.

Leibowitz, H.M., Krueger, D.E., Maunder, L.R. et al. (1980). The Framingham eye study monograph. *Surv Ophthalmol*,**24** (suppl),335-610.

Liu, K., Manton, K.G., & Liu, B.M. (1990). Morbidity, disability and long-term care of the elderly: implications for insurance financing. *Millbank Quarterly*,68,445-92.

Manton, K.G. (1982). Changing concepts of morbidity and mortality in the elderly population. *Milbank Quarterly*,**60**,183-244

Manton, K.G. (1988). A longitudinal study of functional change and mortality in the US. *Journal of Gerontology*,**43**,5153-61.

Manton, K.G. (1990). REVES; Third Workshop, Durham, 1990.

Manton, K.G., & Stallard, E. (1988). *Chronic disease modelling: Mathematics in Medicine No 2*. London, Charles Griffin & Company Ltd.

Martin, J., Meltzer, H. & Elliot, D. (1988). *The prevalence of disability among adults; OPCS surveys of disability in Great Britain*. (Report 1) London: HMSO, 1988.

Mathers, C.D. (1991). *Health expectancies in Australia 1981 and 1988*. Australian Institute of Health: AGPS, Canberra.

Medical Research Council. (1994). *The health of the UK's elderly population*. MRC Topic Review, London, Medical Research Council.

Morgan, K., Dallosso, H.M., Arie, T. et al. (1987). Mental Health and psychological well-being among the old and very old living at home. *British Journal of Psychiatry*,**150**, 801-7.

Morgan, K., Healey, D.W. & Healey, P.J. (1989). Factors influencing persistent insomnia in old age: a follow-up study of good and poor sleepers aged 65-74. *Age and Aging*,**18**, 117-22.

Morgan, K., Dallosso, H.M., Bassey, J. et al. (1991). Customary physical activity, psychological well-being and successful aging. *Aging and Society*,**11**,399-415.

Morris, J.N. & Sherwood, S. (1975). A retesting and modification of the Philadelphia Geriatric Centre morale scale. *Journal of Gerontology*,**130**,77-84.

Moser, K.A., Goldblatt, P.O., Fox, A.J. & Jones, D.R. (1987). Unemployment and mortality: comparisons of the 1971 and 1981 LS census samples. *British Medical Journal*,**294**,86-90.

Mossey, J.M. & Shapiro, E. (1982). Self-rated health: predictor of mortality among the elderly. *American Journal of Public Health*,**72**,800-8.

National Centre for Health Statistics. (1991). *Health: United States, 1990*. Dept of Health & Human Services, PHS 91-1232.

Neugarten, B.L., Havinghurst, R.J. & Tobin, S.S. (1961). The measurement of life satisfaction. *Journal of Gerontology*,**16**,134-43.

Niessen, L.W., Barendregt, J.J., Bonneux, L., & Koudstaal, P.J. (1993). Stroke trends in an aging population. *Stroke*,**24**,931-939.

Nuttall, S.R., Blackwood, R.J.L., Bussell, B.M.H., Cliff, J.P., Cornall, M.J., Cowley, A., Gatenby, P.L., & Webber, J.M. (1993). *Financing long-term care in Great Britain*. Institute of Actuaries.

OECD. (1993). *Health Systems: Facts and Trends, 1960-1991*, Vol I. OECD Paris.

Olshansky, S.J., Rudbery, M.A., Carnes, B.A. et al. (1991). Trading off longer life for worsening health: the expansion of morbidity hypothesis. *Journal of Aging and Health*, **3(2)**,194-216.

OPCS (1993). National population projections. Series PP2. No 18. London HMSO.

OPCS. (1994). Decennial Supplement on Adult Health (to be published)

Pattie, A.H. & Gilleard, C.J. (1979). *Manual of the Clifton Assessment Procedures of the Elderly (CAPE)*. Sevenoaks, Kent: Hodder and Stoughton Educational.

Perenboom, R.J.M., Boshuizen, H.C. & van de Water H.P.A. (1992). Trends in health expectancies in the Netherlands, 1981-1990. In: *Calculation of health expectancies: harmonization, consensus achieved and future perspectives*. Eds Robine J-M, Mather CD, Bone MR, Romieu I. Colloque INSERM/John Libbey Eurotext Ltd.,**226**,309-320.

Pollard, A.H. (1980). The interaction between morbidity and mortality. *Journal of the Institute of Actuaries*,**107**,233-313.

Ritchie, K., Jagger, C., Brayne, C. & Letenneur, L. (1992). Dementia-free life expectancy: preliminary calculations for France and the United Kingdom. In: *Calculation of health expectancies: harmonization, consensus achieved and future perspectives*. Eds Robine J-M, Mather CD, Bone MR, Romieu I. Colloque INSERM/John Libbey Eurotext Ltd.,**226**,233-244.

Robine, J.M. & Ritchie, K. (1991). Healthy life expectancy: evaluation of global indicator of change in population health. *British Medical Journal*,**302**,457-460.

Robine, J.M., & Mathers, C.D. (1993). Measuring the compression or expansion of morbidity through changes in health expectancy. In: *Calculation of health expectancies: harmonization, consensus achieved and future perspectives*. Eds Robine J-M, Mathers CD, Bone MR, Romieu I. Colloque INSERM/John Libbey Eurotext Ltd.,**226**,269-286.

Robine, J.M. & Mormiche, P. (1993). L'esperance de vie sans incapacite augmente. *INSEE PREMIERE: No 281*.

Robine, J.M. & Richie, K. (1993). Measuring changes in population health through disability-free life expectancy calculation: what have we learnt and where should we go? Paper presented at the *IUSSP Conference*, Montreal, August 1993.

Roelands, M., van Oyen, H., & Baro, F. (1994). Dementia-free life expectancy in Belgium. *European Journal of Public Health*,**4**,33-37.

Rogers, A., Rogers, R.G. & Branch, L.G. (1989). A multistate analysis of active life expectancy. *Public Health Report*,**104**,222-225.

Rogers, A., Rogers, R.G., & Belanger, A. (1990). Longer life but worse health? measurement and dynamics. *The Gerontologist*,**30**,640-657.

Roth, M., Huppert, F.A., Tym, E. et al. (1988). *The Cambridge examination for mental disorders of the elderly*. Cambridge: Cambridge University Press.

Sandercock, P.A.G., van den Belt, A.G.M., Linley, R.I., & Slattery, J. (1993). Antithrombotic therapy in acute ischaemic stroke: an overview of the completed randomised trials. *Journal of Neurology, Neurosurgery and Psychiatry*,**56**,17-25.

Sandercock, P.A., & Linley, R. (1993). Management of acute stroke. *Prescribers Journal*, **33**,196-205.

Sanders, B.S. (1964). Measuring community health levels. *American Journal of Public Health*,54(7), 1063-1070.

Schoen, R. (1988). Practical uses of multistate population models. *Ann Rev Sociol* ,**14**:,41-61.

Shipley, M.J., Pocock, S.J., & Marmot, M.G. (1991). Does plasma cholesterol concentration predict mortality from coronary heart disease in elderly people? 18 year follow up in the Whitehall study. *British Medical Journal*,**303**,89-92.

Spagnoli, A. (1991). Clinical relevance in drug trials for Alzheimer's disease and related disorders. *International Journal of Geriatric Psychiatry*,5,265-267.

Sullivan, D.F. (1971). A single index of mortality and morbidity. *HMSA Health Report*,86,347-54.

Tsai, S.P., Lee, E.S. & Hardy, R.J. (1978). The effect of reduction in leading causes of death: potential gains in life expectancy. *American Journal of Public Health*,**68**,996-971.

Tsevat, J., Weinstein, M.C., Williams, L.W., Tosteson, A.N.A., & Goldman, L. (1991). Expected gains in life expectancy from various coronary heart disease risk factor modifications. *Circulation*,83,1194-1201.

Valkonen, T., Sohronen, A.P. & Lahelma, E. (1994). Disability-free life expectancy by level of education in Finland. *The 7th International Meeting of the Network on Healthy Life Expectancy (REVES)* Canberra 1994. (to be published)

van den Berg Jeths, A., Ruwaard, D. & Kramers, G.N. (1994). Health life expectancy in the Dutch document 'Public health Status and Forecasts'. In: *7th Work-group meeting REVES, International Research Network for Interpretation of Observed Values of Healthy Life Expectancy*, Canberra.

van Dijk, P.T.M., Dippel, D.W.J., & Habbema, J.D.F. (1991). Survival of patients with dementia. *Journal of the American Geriatric Society*,**39**,603-610.

van Ginneken, J.K.S., Dissveldt, A.G., van de Water, H.P.A. & van Sonsbeek, J.L.A. (1991). Results of two methods to determine health expectancy in the Netherlands in 1981-1985. *Social Science and Medicine*,**32**,1129-1136.

van Ginneken, J.K.S., Dissevelt, A.G. & Bonte, J.T.P. (1992). Summary of results of calculations of life expectancy free of disability in the Netherlands in 1981-85. In Robine J.M., Blanchet M., Dowd J.E.,eds. *Health Expectancy* (OPCS series SMPS, No 54). London ; HMSO,1992.

van Oyen, H., Roelands, M. & Taffoneau, J. (1994). Regional inequalities in health expectancy in the Netherlands. *The 7th International Meeting of the Network on Healthy Life Expectancy (REVES)* Canberra 1994. (to be published)

Verbrugge, L.M. (1989). Recent, present and future health of American adults. *Annual Review of Public Health*,**10**,333-61.

Weinberger, M., Darnell, J.C., Tierney, W.M. et al. (1986). Self-rated health as a predictor of hospital admission and nursing home placement in elderly public housing tenants. *American Journal of Public Health*,**76**,457-59.

Wilkins, R. & Adams, O.B. (1983). Health expectancy in Canada, late 1970s: demographic, regional, and social dimensions. *American Journal of Public Health*,**73**,1073-80.

Wilkins, R. (1992a). Health expectancy in Quebec,1987. In Robine J.M., Blanchet M., Dowd J.E.,eds. *Health Expectancy* (OPCS series SMPS, No 54). London; HMSO,1992.

Wilkins, R. (1992b). Health expectancy in Canada,1986. In Robine J.M., Blanchet M., Dowd J.E.,eds. *Health Expectancy* (OPCS series SMPS, No 54). London; HMSO,1992.

Wilkins R., Chen J. & Ng E. (1994). Recent trends and longer term prospectives for health expectancy in Canada. *The 7th International Meeting of the Network on Healthy Life Expectancy (REVES)* Canberra 1994. (to be published)

World Health Organization. (1984). *The uses of epidemiology in the study of the elderly*: Report of a WHO Scientific Group on the Epidemiology of Aging. Geneva: World Health Organization, 1984 (Technical Report Series No 706)

Zdeb, M.S. (1977). The probability of developing cancer. *American Journal of Epidemiology*,**106**,6-16.

Appendix A

Table A.1: Overview of questions selected from the Elderly at Home Survey (1976), and the General Household Survey Elderly Sections (1980, 1985, 1991) to measure ability to manage stairs/steps without help

ABILITY TO MANAGE STAIRS/STEPS WITHOUT HELP	Elderly at Home Survey (1976)	GHS Elderly Section 1980	GHS Elderly Section 1985	GHS Elderly Section 1991
Selected question(s)	Can you get up and down stairs or steps (a) on your own without any difficulty, (b) on your own with difficulty, (c) only with help, (d) or not at all?	Do you usually manage to get up and down stairs and steps (a) on your own, (b) only with help from someone else, (c) or not at all?	Do you usually manage to get up and down stairs and steps (a) on your own, (b) only with help from someone else, (c) or not at all?	1. How difficult is it for you to get up and down stairs or steps on your own? (a) Not difficult (b) Quite difficult (c) Very difficult (d) Impossible FILTER: IF VERY DIFFICULT OR IMPOSSIBLE: Do you need anyone to help you getting up and down steps? (a) Yes (b) No (c) Impossible even with help
Recoding	Ability to manage stairs/steps without help? Yes = (a) or (b) No = (c) or (d)	Ability to manage stairs/steps without help? Yes = (a) No = (b) or (c)	Ability to manage stairs/steps without help? Yes = (a) No = (b) or (c)	Ability to manage stairs/steps without help? Yes = 1(a), 1(b), {1(c) and 2(b)} No = 1(d), {1(c) and 2(a)}, {1(c) and 2(c)}

Table A.2: Overview of questions selected from the Elderly at Home Survey (1976), and the General Household Survey Elderly Sections (1980, 1985, 1991) to measure ability to go outdoors without help

ABILITY TO GO OUTDOORS WITHOUT HELP	Elderly at Home Survey (1976)	GHS Elderly Section 1980	GHS Elderly Section 1985	GHS Elderly Section 1991
Selected question(s)	Can you go out of doors (a) on your own without any difficulty, (b) on your own with difficulty, (c) only with help, (d) or not at all?	FILTER: Those who could not manage to get around the house at all and could not manage stairs on their own, were not asked the following question:	FILTER: Those who could not manage to get around the house at all and could not manage stairs on their own, were not asked the following question:	1. How difficult is it for you go outdoors and walk down the road on your own? (a) Not difficult (b) Quite difficult (c) Very difficult (d) Impossible
		Do you usually manage to go out of doors and walk down the road (a) on your own, (b) only with help from someone else, (c) or not at all?	Do you usually manage to go out of doors and walk down the road (a) on your own, (b) only with help fromsomeone else, (c) or not at all?	2. FILTER: IF VERY DIFFICULT OR IMPOSSIBLE: Do you need anyone to help you go outdoors and walkdown the road? (a) Yes (b) No (c) Impossible even with help
Recoding	Ability to go outdoors without help? Yes = (a) or (b) No = (c) or (d)	Ability to go outdoors without help? Yes = (a) No = (b),(c) and those who were not asked the question (see filter)	Ability to go outdoors without help? Yes = (a) No = (b),(c) and those who were not asked the question (see filter)	Ability to go outdoors without help? Yes = 1(a), 1(b), {1(c) and 2(b)} No = 1(d), {1(c) and 2(a)}, {1(c) and 2(c)}

Table A.3: Overview of questions selected from the Elderly at Home Survey (1976), and the General Household Survey Elderly Sections (1980, 1985, 1991) to measure independence in bathing*

INDEPENDENCE IN BATHING*	Elderly at Home Survey (1976)	GHS Elderly Section 1980	GHS Elderly Section 1985	GHS Elderly Section 1991
Selected question(s)	Can you wash yourself (a) on your own without any difficulty, (b) on your own with difficulty, (c) only with help, (d) or not at all?	Do you usually manage to bath, shower, or wash all over (a) on your own, (b) only with help from someone else, (c) or not at all?	Do you usually manage to bath, shower, or wash all over (a) on your own, (b) only with help from someone else, (c) or not at all?	1. How difficult is it for you to wash yourself all over? (a) Not difficult (b) Quite difficult (c) Very difficult (d) Impossible

2. FILTER: IF VERY DIFFICULT OR IMPOSSIBLE: Do you need anyone to help you? (a) Yes (b) No (c) Impossible even with help |
| Recoding | Bathing Independent = (a),(b) Dependent = (c),(d) | Bathing Independent = (a) Dependent = (b),(c) | Bathing Independent = (a),(b) Dependent = (c),(d) | Bathing Independent= 1(a),1(b), {1(c) and 2(b)} Dependent= {1(c) and 2(a)}, {1(c) and2(c)} |

Appendix B

All prevalence figures for NLSAA have been weighted to account for the omission of an institutionalised sample and are the prevalences used for the computation of health expectancies by Sullivan's method.

Table B.1: Age and sex specific prevalence of mental impairment defined by the CAMDEX and by MMSE score of 24 or under (1988 MMAP)

Age (yrs)	Severity of dementia (CAMDEX) % (N)			MMSE score <=24 % (N)
	Minimal	Mild	Moderate/severe	
Males				
75-79	12.0 (29/241)	4.1 (10/241)	1.7 (4/241)	19.5 (56/287)
80-84	6.5 (10/154)	17.5 (27/154)	1.3 (2/154)	32.8 (59/180)
≥85	21.8 (19/87)	8.0 (7/ 87)	4.6 (4/ 87)	47.8 (33/ 69)
Females				
75-79	14.8 (59/400)	3.8 (15/400)	2.8 (11/400)	28.1 (133/473)
80-84	23.2 (73/314)	10.5 (33/314)	4.5 (14/314)	42.5 (144/339)
≥85	38.7 (74/191)	20.4 (39/191)	14.7 (28/191)	70.6 (163/231)

Table B.2: Age and sex specific prevalence of mental impairment defined as IO score of 8 or under for 1981 (MMAP), 1985 (NLSAA) and 1988 (MMAP)

Age (yrs)	IO score 8 or under % (N)		
	1981 (MMAP)	1985 (NLSAA)	1988 (MMAP)
Males			
65-69		4.9 (5/103)	
70-74		6.3 (8/127)	
75-79	5.3 (13/243)	12.4 (14/113)	3.1 (9/287)
80-84	6.6 (6/ 91)	13.8 (8/ 58)	8.3 (15/181)
≥85	15.2 (7/ 46)	23.8 (5/ 21)	11.6 (8/ 69)
Females			
65-69		4.3 (5/116)	
70-74		4.6 (8/173)	
75-79	5.3 (21/394)	10.9 (19/174)	3.8 (18/473)
80-84	6.5 (17/262)	15.3 (21/137)	11.5 (39/339)
≥85	29.9 (50/167)	37.8 (28/ 74)	28.1 (65/231)

Table B.3: Age and sex specific prevalence of visual impairment (defined as difficulty with vision) or institutionalised for 1981 (MMAP), 1985 (NLSAA) and 1988 (MMAP)

Age (yrs)	Visual impairment or institutionalised % (N)		
	1981 (MMAP)	1985 (NLSAA)	1988 (MMAP)
Males			
65-69		16.5 (17/103)	
70-74		13.7 (17/124)	
75-79	25.3 (59/233)	16.1 (18/112)	10.2 (29/285)
80-84	26.2 (22/ 84)	39.7 (23/ 58)	15.2 (27/178)
≥85	42.2 (19/ 45)	61.9 (13/ 21)	22.1 (15/ 68)
Females			
65-69		13.8 (16/116)	
70-74		18.6 (32/172)	
75-79	33.4 (125/374)	30.6 (53/173)	7.0 (33/472)
80-84	40.7 (100/246)	49.6 (67/135)	14.2 (48/339)
≥85	70.6 (113/160)	60.6 (43/ 71)	29.9 (69/231)

Table B.4: Age and sex specific prevalence of hearing impairment (defined as difficulty with hearing) or institutionalised for 1981 (MMAP), 1985 (NLSAA) and 1988 (MMAP)

Age (yrs)	Hearing impairment or institutionalised % (N)		
	1981 (MMAP)	1985 (NLSAA)	1988 (MMAP)
Males			
65-69		34.0 (35/103)	
70-74		26.4 (33/125)	
75-79	43.6 (106/243)	42.9 (48/112)	18.2 (52/285)
80-84	62.6 (57/ 91)	55.2 (32/ 58)	32.6 (58/178)
≥85	71.7 (33/ 46)	76.2 (16/ 21)	54.4 (37/ 68)
Females			
65-69		15.5 (18/116)	
70-74		23.8 (41/172)	
75-79	33.0 (130/394)	35.3 (61/173)	12.7 (60/472)
80-84	43.1 (113/262)	47.4 (64/135)	21.2 (72/339)
≥85	73.1 (122/167)	71.8 (51/ 71)	48.5 (112/231)

Table B.5: Age and sex specific prevalence of urinary incontinence for 1981 (MMAP), 1985 (NLSAA) and 1988 (MMAP)

Age (yrs)	Urinary incontinence % (N)		
	1981 (MMAP)	1985 (NLSAA)	1988 (MMAP)
Males			
65-69		9.7 (10/103)	
70-74		11.3 (14/124)	
75-79	10.7 (26/243)	20.5 (23/112)	8.4 (24/287)
80-84	14.3 (13/ 91)	22.4 (13/ 58)	8.3 (15/180)
≥85	19.6 (9/ 46)	30.0 (6/ 20)	14.5 (10/ 69)
Females			
65-69		18.1 (21/116)	
70-74		22.1 (38/172)	
75-79	8.9 (35/393)	20.8 (36/173)	11.0 (52/471)
80-84	12.2 (32/262)	32.1 (43/134)	15.4 (52/338)
≥85	19.2 (32/167)	37.1 (26/ 70)	23.9 (55/230)

Table B.6: Age and sex specific prevalence of mobility impairment for 1981 (MMAP), 1985 (NLSAA) and 1988 (MMAP)

Age (yrs)	Mobility impairment % (N)		
	1981 (MMAP)	1985 (NLSAA)	1988 (MMAP)
Males			
65-69		1.9 (2/103)	
70-74		4.0 (5/125)	
75-79	2.1 (5/243)	7.1 (8/113)	1.0 (3/287)
80-84	4.4 (4/ 91)	10.3 (6/ 58)	1.7 (3/180)
≥85	2.2 (1/ 46)	14.3 (3/ 21)	7.2 (5/ 69)
Females			
65-69		4.3 (5/116)	
70-74		5.8 (10/172)	
75-79	3.0 (12/394)	6.4 (11/173)	2.1 (10/473)
80-84	3.8 (10/262)	12.7 (17/134)	3.5 (12/339)
≥85	11.4 (19/167)	21.1 (15/ 71)	10.5 (24/228)

Table B.7: Age and sex specific prevalence of difficulty getting out of doors, moderate or severe physical disability (defined by Physical Disability scale) and dependence in 1 or more ADLs (defined by Katz ADL scale) for 1981 and 1988 (MMAP)

Age (yrs)	Difficulty getting out of doors % (N)		Moderate/severe physical disability (Physical Disability Scale) % (N)		Dependence in 1+ ADLs (Katz ADL scale) % (N)	
	1981	1988	1981	1988	1981	1988
Males						
75-79	28.5 (67/235)	24.7 (71/287)	15.2 (37/243)	11.1 (32/287)	13.6 (33/243)	11.1 (32/287)
80-84	38.6 (32/83)	36.7 (66/180)	19.8 (18/91)	21.7 (39/180)	17.6 (16/91)	22.8 (41/180)
≥85	62.2 (28/45)	59.4 (41/69)	37.0 (17/46)	68.7 (27/69)	26.1 (12/46)	29.4 (20/68)
Females						
75-79	35.5 (134/377)	32.3 (153/473)	16.8 (66/393)	12.3 (58/472)	17.3 (68/394)	14.0 (66/473)
80-84	54.0 (134/248)	49.3 (167/339)	27.9 (73/262)	24.8 (84/339)	28.6 (75/262)	25.1 (85/339)
≥85	83.3 (135/162)	77.0 (177/230)	53.9 (90/167)	48.2 (110/228)	53.9 (90/167)	55.9 (128/229)

Table B.8: Age and sex specific prevalence of reduced IADL (defined as unable to perform 2 or more IADLs) and short or critical interval need (1988 MMAP)

Age (yrs)	Reduced IADL % (N)	Short or critical interval need % (N)
Males		
75-79	28.4 (73/257)	76.6 (219/286)
80-84	30.3 (47/155)	75.6 (136/180)
≥85	31.6 (18/ 57)	76.8 (53/ 69)
Females	39.7 (173/436)	
75-79	57.0 (172/302)	26.3 (124/472)
80-84	56.6 (112/198)	39.6 (133/336)
≥85		67.7 (155/229)

Table B.9: Age and sex specific prevalence of poor or fair perceived health for 1981 (MMAP), 1985 (NLSAA) and 1988 (MMAP)

Age (yrs)	Poor or fair perceived health % (N)		
	1981 (MMAP)	1985 (NLSAA)	1988 (MMAP)
Males			
65-69		42.4 (42/ 99)	
70-74		38.1 (45/118)	
75-79	38.3 (93/243)	44.3 (43/ 97)	43.7 (124/284)
80-84	42.9 (39/ 91)	42.0 (21/ 50)	46.7 (84/180)
≥85	37.0 (17/ 46)	35.7 (5/ 14)	41.8 (28/ 67)
Females			
65-69		50.4 (57/113)	
70-74		55.4 (92/166)	
75-79	43.1 (170/394)	54.2 (92/168)	52.1 (245/470)
80-84	45.0 (117/260)	48.4 (60/124)	51.6 (174/337)
≥85	55.4 (92/166)	51.9 (28/ 54)	58.9 (136/231)

Table B.10: Age and sex specific prevalence of depression as defined by SAD scale (1985 NLSAA), depression defined by the CAMDEX and low morale defined by the Philadelphia Geriatric Center Morale scale (1988 MMAP)

Age (yrs)	Depression SAD scale (1985 NLSAA) % (N)	Clinical depression CAMDEX (1988 MMAP) % (N)	Low morale (1988 MMAP) % (N)
Males			
65-69	7.1 (7/ 98)		
70-74	5.1 (6/117)		
75-79	6.1 (6/ 98)	11.6 (28/241)	10.8 (31/287)
80-84	8.0 (4/ 50)	1.9 (3/154)	19.5 (34/174)
≥85	0.0 (0/ 14)	16.3 (14/ 86)	16.9 (11/ 65)
Females			
65-69	14.4 (16/111)		
70-74	11.6 (19/164)		
75-79	10.6 (17/161)	15.8 (63/400)	22.7 (105/463)
80-84	13.0 (15/115)	1.9 (6/313)	23.7 (76/321)
≥85	8.2 (4/ 49)	12.7 (24/189)	38.7 (86/222)

Table B.11: Age and sex specific prevalence of global ill-health for 1981 (MMAP), 1985 (NLSAA) and 1988 (MMAP)

Age (yrs)	Global ill-health % (N)		
	1981 (MMAP)	1985 (NLSAA)	1988 (MMAP)
Males			
65-69		64.7 (67/103)	
70-74		61.3 (77/125)	
75-79	73.6 (176/239)	73.7 (79/107)	58.5 (166/284)
80-84	78.9 (71/ 90)	87.8 (51/ 58)	63.5 (113/178)
≥85	91.3 (42/ 46)	100.0 (21/ 21)	81.2 (56/ 69)
Females			
65-69		68.2 (78/114)	
70-74		73.0 (125/171)	
75-79	71.8 (282/393)	81.0 (141/174)	61.8 (285/461)
80-84	82.2 (212/258)	89.7 (122/136)	67.8 (223/329)
≥85	93.4 (59/167)	95.8 (69/ 72)	83.3 (189/227)

Table B.12: **Age and sex specific prevalence of ill-health defined by Health Index score of 1 or greater for 1985 (NLSAA)**

Age (yrs)	Health Index score ≥1 % (N)
Males	
65-69	90.0 (91/101)
70-74	92.5 (111/120)
75-79	96.2 (103/107)
80-84	94.7 (54/ 57)
≥85	94.9 (19/ 20)
Females	
65-69	94.8 (110/116)
70-74	96.5 (165/171)
75-79	97.6 (165/169)
80-84	99.2 (129/130)
≥85	98.5 (66/ 67)